Rufus

A Boy's Extraordinary Experiences in the Civil War

Phoebe Sheldon

Based on the letters of Rufus Harnden

Brook Hollow Press

Edited by Paul Spector
with additional help from
Betsy Rider, Russell Powell, and Susan Cohen
Layout and cover design by Chris Weeks

brookhollowpress.net

ISBN 978-0-9882357-6-2

Library of Congress Control Number: 2018935004

First edition

Table of Contents

	Introduction	7
1.	I Enlist	10
2.	The Elmira Armory	28
3.	Visit to Washington	42
4.	Soldiers in Camp	51
5.	Bound for Sharpsville	65
6.	Antietam	80
7.	The Field Hospital	105
8.	Harpers Ferry	117
9.	Fever	127
10.	Winter Quarters	136
11.	Virginia Mud	144
12.	Hope landing	153
13.	The Road to Chancellorsville	163
14.	Fairview Farm	168
15.	Another Battle Begins	174
16.	May 2nd	177
17.	May 3rd	197
18.	Campbell Hospital	206
19.	Hospital Scenes	217
20.	Gettysburg	222
21.	New York Harbor	245
22.	Tennessee	261
23.	Chattanooga	273
24.	Lookout Mountain	286
25.	Stonewall	291
26.	Diagnosis	307
	Conclusion	321
	Bibliography	340

Introduction

I was first introduced to Rufus Sayre Harnden by my father, Stanley Sheldon, when he was dying from lung cancer in 1987. My father explained that Rufus, my mother's great grandfather, had fought in the Civil War as a boy and had sent his parents many letters from the front. The letters were saved and passed down through several generations of Rufus's family until they reached my father's hands.

Dad took up an intense study of the collection of these war letters during the last six months of his life. I had the good fortune to spend many hours with him during this time. He read some of the letters out loud to me and he discussed at length the trajectory of Rufus's adventures.

My father had been a popular seventh grade homeroom teacher at The Shady Hill School in Cambridge Massachusetts during the 1950's. Old students of Dad's still approached me on the streets of Cambridge to tell me he was the best teacher they ever had. Among other things, he taught American History. He did this with little use of textbooks. Instead, he and his students read eyewitness accounts, drew maps, constructed tiny cannons, cast and painted lead soldiers, and visited battlefields to stage reenactments of famous engagements.

My mother, siblings, and I were often drawn into these activities. Without even noticing it I developed a deep appreciation of history from primary sources. My father, perched sideways on a chair or even sitting precariously on its back, feet resting upon its seat, with the ever present cigarette dangling as he directed his points, was the conduit for what felt like a thousand and one incredible, often grim, tales about American wars. One of his favorite stories was about the Confederate General Stonewall Jackson's famous flank attack at Chancellorsville. Jackson had pulled off one of the most astounding and brilliantly conceived military maneuvers of the Civil War just before he was mortally wounded at the Battle of Chancellorsville in 1863.

Given my father's scholarly background, it was easy to understand why he was so captivated by the letters during his final months. Not only were they filled with fascinating historical detail, but there emerged from the careful, old fashioned script a touching portrait of a boy of unusual qualities. And it became clear to my father that Rufus had played a key role in an absolutely crucial event at Chancellorsville.

After Dad's death, I inherited a large box of his written material as well as the actual Rufus letters, though I didn't know I had the originals in my possession for almost ten years. I was cleaning my home and listening to Terry Gross interview a person who had started a war letter library when I began to wonder where Rufus's letters might be. I went looking and found, in storage, amidst my father's dusty papers, a faded red manila folder, tied up with pink ribbon. When I opened it, hundreds of handwritten pages spilled out. The yellowed papers were covered in beautiful cursive. Some were folded and torn, many as delicate as dried flowers. Words like Harpers Ferry, Antietam Battlefield, and Chattanooga practically leapt off the pages.

From that moment on I was hooked by the drama and mystery of Rufus Harnden's war experience. I wanted to know who this young man was, what had happened to him, and how he survived the American Civil War.

I began a decades long process of researching Rufus Harnden's role in the war. As I read and reread the letters I found references to people, locations, battles, and other occurrences that eventually provided me with a framework upon which to flesh out his story. By following the history of his regiment, the 107th

NY Volunteers, through the years of 1862 to 1865 I was able to fill in the gaps in the letters and develop a coherent narrative. It was very much like fitting together a puzzle. Eventually I found that I had to tell the story in Rufus's voice or rather I let him tell it through me. The final draft of the narrative portion of the book is approximately half direct quotes from the letters and half me filling in for him to bridge his lapses.

The footnote sections should help the reader discover many of the fascinating details behind the narrative. I found that learning what Rufus was talking about and what he had been through exploded the Civil War from dusty black and white into living color. The war became immediate and real to me, profoundly moving, a lesson in what it means to try to keep one's bearings and survive through the madness that is mass violent conflict: Young men conducted to destruction by older and more powerful men who sit in safety or watch from the hills through their field glasses.

Chapter 1   I Enlist

My name is Rufus Sayre Harnden. Harnden is my father's
last name, Sayre, my mother's maiden name, and Rufus, well,
I am named for a famous abolitionist, so that should tell you
something about me right from the start. Three years ago in 1862,
when I was a boy of seventeen, I tricked myself into going off to
fight in our American Civil War. I went in for the Union side, on
account of I hailed from a small town known as Waverly, situated
in the pretty Chemung River Valley of New York State.

When I joined up the fighting against the secesh states
had gone on already for a year or thereabouts but it was not
progressing very well for our side. The accursed thing seemed to
be getting worse instead of better. What conspired to get me into
the war was this: In June of that year, our noble President, name
of Abraham Lincoln, head of the government in the North and
the best of fellows in my view, put out a call to arms for every
man who could get along. He wanted 300,000 fresh volunteers[1] to
come help him settle the matter with the South once and for all.
It had to be done and the quicker the better.

When the war started up about a year earlier, a few of my
older acquaintances from Waverly went into the Union army, in
what the government called the first wave of volunteers. Then
when Lincoln called for more men in a second wave, a bunch of
us younger boys sure bragged to each other that we wanted to
hop to it and help out our brave friends.

Old Abe (this was how most of us soldier boys referred to our
President) admitted he felt fed up with losing so many battles and
poor generalling[2] and such, as well as the tight political fix he was
in. You see, there were lots of folks in the North who wanted to
forget the Southern debt and come to peaceful terms right away

without any more expenses or loss of life. We called those folks
Southern Sympathizers, Copperhead Snakes, or just Coppers[3] for
short. They were against the war from the very first, the most
of them. Coppers despised Old Abe and blamed him and the
Abolitionists for the war. You'd be surprised how many Coppers
there were in the North at that time. And how miserable they
were making Old Abe's life.

Now in my home, we were every one of us Harndens the
firmest sort of Abolitionists, so Coppers hated us too by all
accounts. My mother told me all about Rufus King who I was
called after, a man who had important things to do with passing
the law to prohibit slavery in the North during the last century.
So, that is how committed my parents felt toward the cause of
justice and no more slavery in the United States, that they would
name their eldest son in his memory. Father and Mother believed
most avidly in fighting for the Union ideals.

As a dutiful son, obviously I didn't care for Coppers much
and I wanted to support both my country and my family as best
I could. I was brought up in a very strict manner. I attended our
Methodist church[4] services regular and meant to dedicate my life
to serving God's purpose, whatever that turned out to be for me
in particular. What made a difficultly for me before I went off to
the army was trying to figure out what in the world God wanted
me to do with myself. I was having trouble arriving at a plan for
my future endeavors.

My father, Dr. Daniel Harnden, was and still is our local doctor
in Waverly.

(I suppose by all this you will correctly infer that I managed to
live through the war and come out the other side. Well, yes I did,
but you will have to wait for the particulars as to how I did it.)

My friends thought Father too strict and an overly pious man
in his ways but it didn't bother me. I'm supposing I was quite

used to him having growed up with him. Father's plan for me was that I learn the drugstore business and eventually set up an establishment as part of his practice. Before I put on the yankee uniform, he got me a place working with our town apothecary, Doc Everett, in his shop, putting up medicines, clerking, and such things as that. I had therefore learnt something of the druggist trade already but tho I greatly enjoyed Doc Everett's company, I did not like it there for most of the time it was dull and tiresome work.

Besides casting about for an exciting but worthy line of work at age seventeen, I was always bothering on about money, especially as the eldest son of the six children in my family. We offspring covered a span of some fifteen years. Next to me came Edwin, then George, Albert, sister Augustus, and finally little brother Henry. Money was tight since there were so many of us to feed and shelter. A village doctor did not earn as well as you might think. Many times Father was paid with a sack of grain or some venison, if he was paid anything at all for his services.

Therefore, as soon as we were able bodied, brother Edwin and I had to labor for the local farmers in their tobacco fields and barns. We earned there what money we could to give to Father and Mother. Of course later, my wages from Doc Everett also went directly into the family coffers.

When along came the government offering to pay[5] a fellow to go off to be a soldier boy, well, fighting for Old Abe and getting paid to do it too seemed like the fairest sort of idea to me. To say nothing of the excitement such a prospect promised.

Adding to my thinking was a simplifying prediction that was widely shared. Every citizen in town agreed that if the President got what he needed in manpower, the war would be over in just three months time. Our newspapers kept us well informed as to how the Southern States did not have the will nor enough resources to fight for their independence much longer.

Soon after Old Abe's June proclamation and call to arms, politicians came along to our village and held rallies explaining what the war effort was lacking, which was mostly us boys, or so they assured us. Large posters went up all over the place with slogans in bold print saying things like STAND BY THE FLAG!! TO ARMS! TO ARMS! and CITIZENS AROUSE!!

The fliers showed us eagles with wings spread and rearing horses while banners flew forth in splendor to appeal to our patriotic emotions. Smaller print explained the bounties we would be paid by New York State and the Union which could amount to $150, a fortune in my young mind. Us boys of Waverly talked ourselves halfway to soldiering before we even took a step in that direction.

The two politicians who came to our town not to just speechify but looking to start their very own regiment were named VanValkenburgh and Diven. I judged VanValkenburgh to be the older, in his forties. He was a tall man generously padded around the middle. Diven I thought to be perhaps thirty years of age and smaller in height and bulk. Both were honorable congressmen for New York but now left their Washington duties to work for the greater cause. They puffed the war and each other about what a fine regiment they were raising and what an honor it would be to be led to glory by who else? Themselves, of course.

My friends and I laughed plenty at their blowing so much hot air but we still thought we might surely try to go, having caught such large cases of the war fever as it raged throughout the countryside. Three months of our lives did not seem like any very great sacrifice. I imagined how fine it would feel to send the bounty money home to Father, as well as the thirteen dollars they promised in monthly pay for a corporal's wage. So everything just fit together of a piece to guide me onto the path of soldiering for the Union.

One large problem contrary to my thoughts was that many of us younger Waverly boys were not yet of an age[6] to go for a soldier. Eighteen years was required to join up plus a parent's consent. And it turned out that my father and mother, tho each so unfailingly patriotic, were dead set against me going in particular. Father said that I was not growed enough nor was my constitution strong enough to endure soldiering. It's true I'm not a large person, about five and a half foot in height, nor very fleshy, but I felt I was fit, knew how to fire his rifle and even ride a horse. Of course, I thought I was growed enough for anything.

Tho down deep, I knew he might be right as to the state of my constitution and youthfulness, I hated to admit it and his words greatly offended my boyish pride. I began pestering him to make him think I wanted to go awful bad. Looking back on it, I guess I had to prove to him that I could measure up. I harassed and teased and coaxed while inside I was not sure that I did actually mean to sign up when it came to the point. Lets just say that I harbored many fears and doubts as to what I should do if push came to shove.

Around that same time, my two very closest friends and childhood playfellows, Will Tenbrook and Joe Pickering, both seventeen like me and from good Methodist families, made the decision to get along over to Elmira where the big state armory[7] lay, tell a fib about their ages, and try to enlist.

Now both of them boys were large, larger than myself. Tenbrook in particular was exceptionally strong and fine in his form, equal and willing to take on any physical task. Tenbrook grew up on a farm just outside of town. His wavy hair was bleached to straw by sunshine and mostly fell in his eyes which were an airy blue. His nature was sweet and strong in equal proportion. Many is the time I have seen girls from the village dawdle along the side of a field just to get a sneak peek at Will working a row in his britches. He could pick me up and sling me across his shoulders like any old bale of hay just for fun. Then there was Joe, a town boy like myself, taller but thin and wiry. Thoughtful in person, often troubled by anxious thoughts but also given to flights of exceedingly good humor. He frequently kept me and Tenbrook in states of the highest amusement. I was fondest of these two out of all my acquaintances. Well, I just had to go along with them to Elmira.

I informed my father that they were planning this trip and that I was determined to accompany them but would probably not stay if he was still so strong set against it. Actually, I was leaning to not staying because of my own deepening doubts as to my constitution. I worried about my stamina in the face of a soldier's challenges.

"Father," says I, "I'll just go over for the trip and come straight back if you insist. But I want to go for a soldier soon. Will and Joe have their parents blessing in this."

And Father says back to me once again, as he has said so many times, "Rufus, my boy, you are not as physically grown as those two boys, I am concerned that the many difficulties of a soldier's life will wear on you excessively."

"Well Father, I think that if I am strong enough to work the tobacco fields then I am strong enough for a soldier's life and I just wish you and Mother could see the thing in that light!"

It was at that very moment Father took me by absolute surprise. He said, "Oh all right, go if you must!" and he signed the consent form on the spot. The look on his face was one of frustration and exhaustion mixed.

Well, he had me then. I had pushed him too hard and I hated to back out after that. I had got myself into a bad fix on account of wanting to make a big show of my manly courage and sticking tight with my best friends.

1. 300,000 Fresh Volunteers

During the summer of 1862 President Lincoln asked the Northern states to provide more men for the war effort. Each state was required to fill a large quota of new soldiers for this 2nd wave of volunteers. A draft did not exist at this time. On July 1st he issued the official call to arms. Men and boys poured from their towns and farms to do their patriotic duty, even before the request became official. From 1861 to 1865 approximately 2.6 million men went to fight for the Union and considerably less, about 1 million, fought for the South. New York State ultimately provided the most men for the Union cause, 400,000 out of a population of 3,800,000, and subsequently lost the most men to violent death and disease.

2. Poor Generalling and Such

In June of 1862, just before young Rufus left his home and marched off to the war, Confederate President Jefferson Davis had selected a new general to take over the South's main army. And what a general the formidable and extraordinarily gifted Robert E. Lee was turning out to be. President Davis made a wise choice in finding a commander who knew how to exploit the weaknesses of his adversaries to the hilt. Ironically in 1861, during the lead up to outright war with the Southern States, President Lincoln had tried to appoint the same Robert E. Lee, a 30 year veteran of the federal army, to be the head of the Union Army. General Lee had cordially declined the invitation, feeling that his allegiance to his beloved home state of Virginia took precedent over his service in the federal government. Lincoln remained bitterly aware of this loss throughout the next four terrible years of civil war as he struggled to find generals half as competent as Lee.

By the summer of 1862 when Rufus joined the Union Army, Lee, with his two loyal generals, Stonewall Jackson and James Longstreet, commanding the left and right wings of his army, had humiliated the Union in several recent battles. He had done this with an army not only smaller than the Union armies but less well equipped and supplied. And to make matters worse, Lee was now poised to begin an invasion into Maryland, the first time the South would threaten to take control of a neutral state. Lee meant to bring the war to the North's very doorstep, if not over it in an effort to humiliate and defeat the Union seat of government in Washington.

3. Copperheads

The people in the North who were against the Civil War were called Copperheads, the name of a poisonous snake, by their opponents, and Peace Democrats by their supporters. These people wanted an immediate settlement with the South, the removal of Lincoln and his Republican Party from office, and no emancipation for the slaves. They blamed the war entirely on Lincoln and the Abolitionists and wanted to turn the clock back to an earlier time, when the States were allowed more self determination to govern themselves without interference from the federal government.

4. Methodist Church

This was a branch of Protestantism that had been founded in England during the 1700's. Missionaries brought it across the Atlantic to the colonial United States where it found fertile ground, especially among the growing middle classes in the North, probably because Methodist philosophy put great emphasis on an individual's hard work and service to others, traits that were absolutely essential for the building of community and responsible citizenship in the fledgling democracy. Methodists were dedicated to notions of service, piety, and the belief that salvation was achievable through the practice of these principles. This made Methodists adhere to notions of personal sacrifice and also enthusiastic supporters of emancipation for people in slavery. They became very active in the underground railroad, helping to transport escaping slaves away from the South toward their freedom in the Northern states or Canada.

Even though he was only 17, Rufus went to war armed with a belief system that would provide him support for service to what he perceived to be a just cause, and with a family and a strong social network at home that would remind him constantly where his priorities lay. In that he was lucky; it was far more than most men carried with them into the deadly vortex of the Civil War.

5. Three Months of War

It was widely assumed in the North that the South had neither the resources nor the heart to fight a long expensive war. At the onset of hostilities, though the South had more square miles of territory to its name, it contained only half as much population as the North. And almost half of that population, a staggering 40%, was enslaved and in no way interested in supporting a culture that intended to continue inflicting oppression and misery on them. Additionally, the South was stuck in an agricultural age during a time of booming industrial development in the North. The Northern states had more workers, more money, more railway lines, more factories, more products, and interestingly and very importantly, more food. Though the rural South grew the lion's share of the six leading agricultural cash crops in the US, only one of those was actually edible, and that was rice.

It was therefore understandable that common wisdom in the North held that the war would not last very long. The popular impression was that the agrarian, backward, and ill-supplied rebels could be quickly subdued and life would return to good order.

The original goal of the federal government in 1861 was only to put down the insurrection and win the loyalty of the Southern people back to the enduring and lofty ideals of popular government, equal rights, and the dignity of workers, as put forth in the United States Constitution. The Federal goal did not include occupying the South or taking away its slaves. The dominant prediction in the North was that ninety days of war with minimal strife was all it would take to subdue the rebellious Southern states.

Unfortunately, the Southerners had their own version of the delusion. They maintained that their tough 'Johnny Rebs' could whip the city-softened 'Billy Yanks' and send them mewling back to their mothers' knees where they belonged. The secessionists felt that they were defending a noble way of life after all, one that included the institution of slavery but was much more than that to them.

Jefferson Davis and the leaders and generals of the Confederacy still imagined in 1862 that the North would not fight too hard to hold on to the South. Their goal was to break the will of the Northerners and gain, not necessarily territory, but freedom from what they perceived to be tyranny. If General Lee could fight his way into Washington, he figured that he could force the Northern fighters and Abraham Lincoln, folks he called with an air of reserved detachment, 'those people,' to stand down.

Perhaps these delusions explain to some degree why the politicians on both sides were able to whip up so much support for the war in the first place. Both sides predicted it was going to be short, triumphant, and relatively easy because their opponents were obviously so weak. All the best parts of a picture book war were emphasized: dressing up, parading, flag waving, cheering, group activities, winning; it sounded more like summer camp than warfare to boys like Rufus and his friends.

Rufus's group of civilians volunteers from Waverly knew very little about soldiering or what would be required of them once they enlisted. Though some of them owned weapons and had grown up using them to hunt in the fields and woods outside of town, they had never turned a gun on another human being. Even most of the training for the New York State militia went no further than six days a year of drill practice, one week of camping out, and the odd march around the town common. But, their Southern opponents came primarily from a huge class of unpropertied white males who knew all about waging a determined war on other human beings, as they had been waging one for years on the enslaved black people of the South.

Two thirds of the white population in the South owned no land of their own. This class of people lived a hard-scrabble life of subsistence farming on leased land, hunting, guarding plantations, and chasing down runaway slaves for the wealthy land owners. Tracking and catching fleeing slaves was a full time occupation for many of these civilian men. They were called Slave Patrollers and had the authority to stop and arrest any slave they thought had violated the slave code. Beyond that they could inflict sever punishment, mutilation, even death.

These poor white southerners were tough as nails by well-earned reputation. They had been hunting, riding, and using firearms all their lives. They knew how to handle horses well, live off the land, and travel with few possessions. There was no such class of fighting men among the population in the North because there had not been any serious threat to peace in a long time.

6. Army Bounty and Pay

A volunteer like Rufus was offered not only a monthly salary but extra money for signing up for a three year period of service; this was called a 'bounty.' The state allotted $50 per man and the federal government promised another $100 for a grand total of $150 in bounty which was a lot of money in those days, especially for a teenager. Each dollar was worth about 20 modern dollars. Many soldiers enlisted purely for the opportunity to have a steady job and a paycheck. Once a man was in the Union Army, he would receive $13 a month (unless he was black in which case he received about $7). A Confederate soldier in the South received slightly less than $13 a month. By 1864 the amount had been increased in the North to $16 dollars a month for all enlisted men regardless of color. By that time, 10% of the Union army was made up of black volunteers. In 1862, a colonel like Diven received $212 and a general got as much as $758 per month. Payday was supposed to come every two months but it was rarely as regular as that and it commonly came very late. In particularly difficult times, it did not come at all.

7. Age of Civil War Combatants

Almost a third of the all the men who fought in the Civil War were under the age of 18, at least when they first went up to enlist. Of the total of 3.5 million men who fought in the war, 1 million were, like Rufus, not yet 18 years old. Most of the really young boys entered the army as musicians, not as soldiers, though many of them did eventually make their ways into the fighting ranks. The federal army had positions for 40,000 musicians and the government saw nothing wrong with filling those positions with boys who at least on paper would not be going into combat. There was no thought given to what these young men and children would be exposed to when the fighting started. At the time, there was simply no understanding of the effects that traumatic events could inflict on the nervous system of a soldier, nor was there any knowledge about the fact that a man's age, or lack of it, could determine the probability of his being disabled by such trauma. The Civil War was nicknamed 'The Young Man's War' because so many of its combatants were still boys or teenagers.

8. The NY State Armory

The armory itself was a large building with outlying structures that contained all things related to the military aspects of the state of New York. There were barracks for the recruits and officers, storage spaces for uniforms and arms, stables for horses and mules, and offices filled with clerks and paperwork. Rufus had to fill out a surprisingly large amount of paperwork to enlist, as did they all. The Elmira armory encampment, thirty acres in size, lay along the side a freshwater pond called Foster Pond. With the steady accumulation of a large number of recruits, more and more latrines were built nearby and put to heavy use. The water in the pond soon became contaminated with bacteria.

Two years later, in 1864, the army converted the large site into a prisoner of war camp called Elmira Prison. Some 12,000 rebel fighters were incarcerated there. A quarter of them died from the abysmal conditions in the camp which included malnutrition, exposure, and water borne disease.

Abraham Lincoln, President of the Union

Robert E. Lee

THE COPPERHEAD PARTY.——IN FAVOR OF *A VIGOROUS PROSECUTION OF PEACE!*

Copperheads

Portrait of a young Stonewall Jackson

Young Soldier

Recruitment posters

Young Musician

Chapter 2   The Elmira Armory

Some days later in July, after my father signed the consent, Will, Joe, and I set off to walk the many hot, dusty miles over to Elmira and become Union soldiers. I had only a pocket watch, the clothes on my back, some apples, a canteen of water, and my father's revolver wrapped in a rag. I did not have bullets for the handgun because Father couldn't afford to purchase any. Will and Joe carried no more than I, tho each had a few cents to buy food off a farmwife if need arose. We laughed the whole way, full of high talk as boys will be, about how we were going to whip the johnny rebs, send them skedaddling back down to Dixie and be great heroes.

When we got there, I found my shoes was worn through the bottoms, being old in the first place. Will and Joe thought it mean that my father hadn't provided me with better footwear nor even any money at all.

Elmira turned out to have boys like ourselves pouring into it from towns and farms all over the state. It was nothing for us to follow the noisy crowds to the big armory which sat at the edge of the town by a lake they called Foster Pond. That armory was a busy place, filled with dirt and folks, some in uniform but mostly out, all lolling about in the summer heat with little to do but make mischief is what it looked like to me. We took some time searching amidst the chaos to find the political men who had come to Waverly to raise our regiment.

At last we found the younger one named Diven in a building where the offices lay. He sat us down to fill out papers on ourselves which we started in on but then Joe stopped writing.

He said to us, "Rufus, Will, I'm thinking I want to go home. I'm sorry but this place is awful rough. It worries me quite a bit."

That much was obvious and worrisome to me also, and I said as much.

Then Will says to Joe, "If you feel that way Joe maybe you shouldn't come along, for it will surely get rougher than it is here once we get to the fight."

Joe just nodded. He got up quietly and ducked out of the room, telling us he'd wait for us elsewhere. Diven let Joe back out without much fuss.

Again, I thought to go with him but I got to talking more to Will and thinking about it further and thoughten how everyone at home would laugh and make fun of me if I did, especially after all my carrying on and big talk, so I stayed to see it through. It was not so bad after all, only three months. We should be home by planting time in the spring. Will and I thought we had a neat little plan all figured out.

We three friends said our goodbyes right there outside the office. I sure hated to see Joe start off for home. A few months later, he changed his mind again and joined up with another New York regiment, the 141st, sister regiment to ours. So he come along to the war after all in the end. But now I look back on it, I realize that I never did lay eyes on Joe after that parting. We corresponded but Tenbrook and I would never see Joe in this world again.

After we signed those papers with the details of our personal information including the white lies about our age, Diven put the last enlisting paper down before us. Now it was written there clear as day "for a period of three years." I took pause with my hand hovering above the page as did Will but then we looked each other in the eye and came to a silent agreement. Three years did not seem so very long if it meant we could save the country and be heroes, so we signed and clinched the deal with our Uncle Sam.

Then Diven walked the two of us new recruits to a long wooden shed where he said we was to stay and sleep on the floor as best we could, all the cots being taken up by then. He told us the armory would be full in ten days or so. We had eighty men in our company already and more coming in all the time.

After Diven left us, me and Will were pretty much on our own hook. I sat down first thing and penned a letter to my father asking for boots since I had no money to buy me some.

It turned out lucky I had Will for a best friend because it sure proved to be hard in those barracks. Folks would steal anything that you laid down even for a second. There was card games being played constantly, tobacco being smoked or chawed, and boys fighting over nothing. I came in for a fair bit of teasing on account of the sorry state of my flapping shoe leather. Will kept me well out of it tho. All he had to do was stand up next to me and those ruffians would back off directly without a word, even sometimes a mumbled apology. I was much beholding to him.

Further difficulties were they served three meals a day but the food wasn't much to speak of, plus the latrine ditches were full to over-flowing and the air very close. Will and I got hungry and sick of that filthy place in no time.

Too make matters worse, a few days along, both of us developed what I learnt was a case of the curse of soldiers[1]. No matter the color of your uniform, blue, grey, or purple, you will get the runs and have to hop over to the latrines a good deal if you are in the army. I found myself hitching up my trousers as I began to get whittled down from what the boys around there called the " two step." I had to go over to the armory drug store and beg some medicine I thought might help it.

Will and I couldn't find any type of religious services which might keep us honest and out of trouble so we asked Diven if we might go home for some days instead of wait around in such an unhealthy place. He told us to apply for a furlough, which was what he called it, permission to go off from the army. We did so and got one.

Instead of going straight home we journeyed down to the city of Auburn to see the sights and have some fun. We had neither of us been on our own in a town of that size. With no money to speak of we couldn't do any harm to ourselves, so we walked around and watched the townsfolk go about their business. Then we made our way to visit our families in Waverly once more and so I could try to find some boots. I couldn't get hold of any that fit me and had to settle for another pair of old shoes handed down from a cousin. Mother hadn't forgiven me for enlisting but she kindly fed me up so that I could gain back the weight I'd lost. Father still seemed greatly put out over my actions. He was quite severe in his dealings with me.

We were gone from Elmira a week or ten days and generally kicked around. When we got back after our trip, we found a bunch of our other friends from Waverly had come into the armory while we were away. There were Will Edgerton and little Henry Smith, ages seventeen like me and Tenbrook. Then John Wiggens who was twenty-four and a married man with a wife Mary and babe at home on his farm. Also and lastly Abe Decature, a friend of my father's, age thirty-nine, married with a large family of his own. I think he partly come along to look after us younger boys. Decature was the only one of us who actually owned a rifle and had marched in our local militia, but the militia boys never had done any fighting in my lifetime. It was that civilized in our part of New York State.

They were all topnotch men, Methodist and God fearing, except Wiggins who reminded me quite a bit of brother Edwin, the family cut-up. Will Edgerton I knew fairly well. His family circumstances were much more difficult that mine ever even got close to. Because of a wayward father, it seemed the whole burden of caring for his mother and little sisters had fell upon his shoulders. He was very tall, stooping, and worried about money most all the time. His face set in a permanent expression of frown, like he was trying to solve a vexing problem. Which I guess he was, being almost an overly loving son, if such a thing is possible. From the start of his arriving at the armory, he received almost daily letters of complaint and fret from his mother. Letters he in turn fretted over profoundly as he sat to pen his replies.

Whereas there was Wiggins. He was a dark-haired, wiry elf of a man of average height who seemed larger on account of his outsized personality and his unusually care free smile. Light on his feet and quick with a joke, he thought nothing of firing up a smoke, taking a swig off a jug, and digging into a good card game with no care for consequences to speak of. My father had never approved of my keeping close company with Wiggins but I liked him a good deal and couldn't help it.

This is how Wiggins could carry on, "Harnden," he'd sing out to me, "Life might be short, best try to make it a little sweeter. You are too God inclined by half. Here, have a taste of my smoke!" and he would stuff his cigar right into my mouth and laugh heartily over it.

Even Tenbrook enjoyed a smoke now and then, so it wasn't long before I couldn't resist any further and I started up one or two myself. I was surprised to find that a smoke calmed my state of unpleasantly high excitement over the unpredictability of my new situation. Old straight laced Decature shook his head but he swore he wouldn't tattletale to my father. Truth be told, there wasn't a man in the company besides myself but what played cards, religious or otherwise. It seemed all the boys had to work hard at various vices to calm their nerves and let off steam. I made up my mind to never play a game of cards, and I was going to stick to that, at least.

We was one day paid ninety dollars towards our bounty. Edgerton and I sent all of ours home for our families' use and I was sure proud to have done it, just like I thought I would be in my imaginings. Perhaps my father would come to see that what I had done was a good thing and I was making myself useful.

By the 10th of August, we were full up at the armory. Not only that but we were the first bunch in the North to reach the thousand men needed to form a completed regiment[2] and so they told us we got the honor of being called henceforth "The Banner Regiment." Hearsay informed us that we were bound for the war by way of the capital city of Washington, beyond that there was no word shared with us as to a final destination, or even which part of which Union army we was to join. I began to suspect that the lowly infantryman was expected to accept a strange state of not knowing much about his fate.

When we was to arrive in Washington[3], I heard that the President himself would congratulate us on our patriotism for being the earliest of the Second Wave of recruitments to put into the field.

A few days later, on August 13th, the army gave us our uniforms[4], loaded us down with all sorts of field equipment but no arms, and then officially mustered us into the 107th New York Volunteer Infantry. We were real soldiers at last.

Diven went in as our Colonel. VanValkenburgh was also appointed Colonel but ranked above Diven. We were in Company A in which there were one hundred men, quite a few from the Waverly area. I knew a good deal of them, perhaps a twenty by name and forty by sight. I thought the army wanted to keep us boys who knew each other together for our spirits. Captain Wilkerson was our company commander. Our company chaplain was Captain Crane and he came from Elmira as did Wilkerson. I wasn't acquainted with either of them before that time. The regiment had ten companies in it. We also had a large band and the most of our officers were mounted on fine horses.

I'd stood up to be a soldier and now I began to believe it, whereas before it didn't seem like the real thing while we was hanging around the armory doing nothing in our civilian duds for the better part of a month.

I got two coats, one lighter of jacket length, and one very long and heavy, both of them dark blue. My trousers were light blue with a stripe up each side to the waist. My blouse was a simple shirt and they gave me just one pair of drawers to wear under my trousers. There was also a pair of socks and finally some boots though they did not fit me well and gave me cause to worry about them straight off, because I knew we were at least in for a lot of long marches to reach the environs of the war. A small slouch cap finished the project of dressing me. The uniform was uncomfortable and rough made but I knew it was a sight better than the homespun grey those reb boys were said to wear.

On top of the clothing was where the real trouble got started in terms of things for us to tote. A heavy wool blanket, another blanket but rubberized on one side, a knapsack, a canteen, a pan and fork, a knife, another sack lined with rubber called a haversack for carrying our food rations. There were no guns or ammunition as yet. All this added up to weigh what I judged to be over thirty pounds if not more for us to sling around on our marches.

1. The Curse of the Soldiers

Dysentery thrived in the semi-squalid conditions of Civil War encampments. It was caused by a toxic bacteria that produced symptoms in the intestine of an infected person, giving the unfortunate sufferer chronic diarrhea. The soldiers called it 'the two-step' or 'quickstep' for obvious reasons. Dehydration, weight loss, or secondary infections like pneumonia eventually killed one out of ten men who contracted a serious case of dysentery. It was a great deal more than just a nuisance for a Civil War soldier, and, though Rufus thought his father knew of a medicine that might slow it down, in reality there was no known cure at the time.

During the 1860's, doctors could not come up with effective treatments for infections because they had no idea that tiny invisible bacteria caused illness. It is said that the Civil War was the last war fought in 'the dark ages of medicine,' because so little was known of germs and the real causes of illnesses like dysentery, camp fever, measles, small pox, or even the dreaded gangrene that got into the soldiers wounds and killed them off in droves. It was not until 1876 that it was finally established that tiny microbes could spread through dirt, air, water, or body fluids and cause a world of trouble.

The dysentery that Rufus got was spread primarily through fecal contamination of the water supply. Camps like the armory in Elmira were established close to streams or other sources of water out of necessity, and their latrines were then set up relatively close to camp, out of convenience and ignorance. Hence the latrines and large areas where men, horses, and mules defecated were close enough to the water supplies like Foster Pond to contaminate them.

Soldiers knew of no reason to boil drinking water and so, once a water source became infected with toxic bacteria, illness spread quickly through the populations of men living nearby in crowded conditions. Added to contaminated water, other sources that contributed to the epidemics of disease that swept through the armies were dirty cooking and washing pans (often the same pan was used for both), filthy hands, spoiled food, and insects.

In fact, infections killed far more Civil War soldiers than did actual battles. Of the total of 3.5 million men who fought and the approximately 750,000 who died, more fell to disease than were lost in battle. At any given time an unbelievable one in four soldiers was suffering from dysentery to some degree or other.

2. A Completed Regiment

The regiment was the principal fighting unit that a Civil War general used to deploy his battle plan out in the field. Theoretically a regiment had 1000 men in it and was divided into ten companies of 100 men each. Each company could be further broken down into 2 squads of 50, each under the command of a captain, for special assignments, like picket duty. The structure of a Civil War army was complicated and confusing, not just for the families at home but often for the soldiers themselves as commanders were changed constantly, units re-assigned, and men dropped out due to illness, injury, or unauthorized leave, something that was taken all too frequently. The discipline problems of Civil War armies on both sides of the war were legendary.

If one looked at a Civil War army as a pyramid with a President and commanding general at the very top and as many as 100,000 individual men at the bottom, then just below the top commanders would be the first level of subdivisions called the 'Corps,' a word from the French language meaning 'body.' The main rebel army had 3 big Corps and Union armies could have many smaller sized Corps. The different Corps were identified by number as in 1st, 2nd, 3rd, 4th, etc.

Each Corps had some rank of general in command, usually a major general. A Corps in the Union army would typically have between five and ten thousand men in it, whereas a Corps in the southern army could have well over twenty thousand men in it.

Each Corps was then subdivided into Divisions at the next level down, most commonly three in number, also commanded by a major general, and identified by a symbolic patch sewn on the uniform. Rufus was in the Red Star Division of the 12th Corps and so sported a red cotton star on his sleeve. It came to be called "the Bloody Star Division."

A Division was in turn comprised of between 2 and 4 Brigades, each with a brigadier general in charge, and finally a Brigade was composed of 4 to 6 Regiments, each under the command of a colonel. Finally, a regiment was divided into the various companies identified by alphabetical letters, each under the command of a lieutenant or captain.

3. Washington

The Washington of 1862 that the 107th NY regiment marched into was a city in the midst of rapid transformation. When the war first broke out, it had been a sleepy, rural town, a capital city in name only, sandwiched between Maryland, a neutral state, and Virginia, a slave state. It lay upriver from the mouth of the Potomac River on the north shore. During the humid summer months most of the population of several thousand left the city for cooler, pleasanter environs elsewhere. The capitol buildings were as yet only in the process of being built. But both the Union and the Confederate sides wanted to claim the highly symbolic location for their own. In 1861, rebel soldiers massed outside it in preparation for seizure and occupation but Union troops were able to save it at the last minute. Nevertheless, much of the city remained sympathetic to the South's cause throughout the first year of the war.

By 1862, it had become a staging area for the Union war machine, with only small pockets of sympathizers remaining. The population swelled with crowds of soldiers, civilians, and freed slaves. New infrastructure of roads, depots, and buildings enveloped the town. The Capitol dome rose above the city like a beacon. Following the close call in 1861, Lincoln ordered that 33 miles of defenses be built on both sides of the river for the protection of his seat of government.

4. Uniforms and Equipment

The blue uniform of the federal infantryman included a heavy overcoat for cold weather and a short, lighter coat called a 'sack' coat because of the rough cotton material it was made from, both dyed a dark blue. A pair of light blue trousers with a stripe up each side, a shirt known as a 'blouse,' one pair of underwear called 'drawers,' one pair of socks, some boots, and a small lightweight blue cap completed the outfit.

The hat was called a 'kepi' or more commonly a 'forage cap.' It came from a french design for a small, flat topped military hat with a short visor. The Civil War version was made from soft cloth and tended to slump forward or to the side and was worn in both armies, hence its other name, the 'slouch cap.'

A wool blanket, a rubberized blanket to be used as a ground cloth, poncho, or even a makeshift tent, a large, soft knapsack, a canteen, a pan, some eating utensils, a knife, and a rubber-lined food bag for carrying rations called a haversack to be worn across the shoulder on the side, were all the items Rufus would use to camp with and feed himself in the field. For fighting, he would later be given a belt with his bayonet and its scabbard, a cap box to hang on the belt, a cartridge box slung on another strap across his shoulders, and of course, a rifle.

The rebel soldiers were not clothed as well as their Northern contemporaries. Though the South had plenty of cotton, it did not have the manufacturing capacity to produce uniforms of good quality or consistency. Their uniforms were dyed grey or brownish grey, often called 'butternut' after a squash that was used as a dye. They were usually cut from homespun materials and made at home.

"Grand Review" of the Union Army in Washington

Lincoln in his top hat

Union Soldiers' Uniforms

A Young Soldier's Equipment

Col. VanValkenburgh of the NY 107th

Chapter 3   Visit to Washington

When we was all officially donned in the blues, equipped, loaded, and lined up for our oaths we looked a proud and happy bunch. After the swearing in, we gave a loud cheer and tossed our hats in the air.

Tenbrook clapped me hard enough on the back to take my breath away in his enthusiasm.

I told him, " Save your strength for whipping rebs!"

This remark only succeeded in prompting him to laugh, then grab me round the waist and lift me off my feet announcing as he did so for all around to hear,

"Don't worry about me! Why I'll carry you all the way to Dixie. I could you know!"

Of course Wiggins was close by and laughed his head off.

Then the officers tried to march the entire regiment off to the railroad depot[1].

Well, with not one stitch of training, we made a mess of things from the start. And how did they imagine it could have been otherwise? We hadn't been shown a whit about marching or formations or anything! Our officers bellowed out orders that we simply didn't comprehend. The boys sure had to learn there and then how to march four abreast in file to a pace set out by our drummers which took some doings to achieve, I can tell you. But we finally got the hang of it well enough to get along down the road.

At the station, we forgot our recent struggles and became highly excited to climb into the train cars at about midnight, first time I ever traveled that way, it being such a new mode of transport.

They handed out one loaf of bread and one half pound of salt pork to each of us for our haversacks as we boarded for the trip as far as Baltimore. This was the index of the soldier's life and there was some grumbling I can tell you, especially from Wiggins who, tho a tough sort in many ways, was already finding fault with soldiering.

Myself, the two Wills, Wiggins, Henry, and Decature stuck together like burs on the journey, crammed up against each other on the narrow benches. It was a hot night but the open windows let in a rush of cool air that allowed us to doze off and on until dawn broke. Then we seen that we was passing through Pennsylvania and it was the most beautiful, lush countryside I or any of us ever saw.

Wherever a citizen stood out in a field or was abroad in a road, he or she would stop whatever they was doing and wave a hat or an encouraging handkerchief in our direction. When we pulled into a station for a minute or two, folks came to the open windows and handed through cups of water and gifts of food, which was lucky because we had most of us run out of water in the heat of the rail cars traveling under that blazing sun.

We felt appreciated all the way down to Maryland, arriving in Baltimore at about one o'clock in the morning on a Thursday night. We had a cold bite furnished by the citizens and marched down the street. Along the way we were attacked by the welcoming mob in perfect order. It being so late we did not expect much but the population jumped from their beds when they heard our brass band to wave flags from every window almost. Then we took the rail cars bound again for Washington city built on the banks of the great Potomac River.

We got into that town at noon and went to dinner furnished by the government. I think we all had to stand up to eat meat that would crawl, sour bread, and the worst stuff you wouldn't call coffee I ever saw. That completed the meal. Out of a thousand men, I don't think one hundred touched it.

Later we had supper of the same awful kind and then we did our level best to march neatly past the President who stood up on the steps of the domed capital building which was being erected to hold the Union government.

He was the tallest man around, dressed in black with a top hat which made him seem even taller, like a man out of a story book. He took off the hat as we come along. I judged him to be every bit as noble looking and of great character as I had previously imagined. All the boys were as impressed as I on this point.

We assembled in the road before Old Abe and his many attendants and officers. Then the President gave our two commanders, VanValkenburgh and Diven, the banner they had promised us, and he talked some about honor and duty to the flag, and how we was the best regiment in the field, but I couldn't hear the most of it, there being so many people about the place. After that, we was officially known as the 107th New York Volunteer Infantry Banner Regiment. The good Captain Wilkerson informed me that we had 1014 men, counting officers. I constantly peppered that man with questions but he didn't seem to mind me much. He was very kind throughout my dealings with him at that time and sometime later I sure hope I made it up to him.

Once we were reviewed by Old Abe, our officers led us through the city along a wide avenue. Our regimental band struck up 'Dixie' as we traveled down that street toward a vast wooden bridge that would carry us across the wide Potomac into the Union occupied State of Virginia. We felt as fresh and ready for war as anyone and one and all wore a look of pride and exhilaration.

The citizenry lined the way and cheered us along until we got out onto the bridge and left them behind. The Captain told me that bridge was called the Long Bridge[2] on account of its length of over a mile. There were places in the planking where you could see they was able to take some of it up at night so that rebs or traitor citizens couldn't sneak across and do their mischief in the city under cover of darkness. When we crossed that bridge, we were crossed over into what they called the theater of war. As we marched along the sun sank over the horizon lending a sobering mood to our journey toward the enemy.

Once we got off the bridge, it was dark enough to be disorienting. I judged we then marched four or five miles to take our night's rest upon the open ground under the stars. By the morning light we found ourselves stationed near a large fort named Fort Albany at Arlington Heights[3]. The Heights were long high bluffs running alongside the river. Our camp went by the title Camp Seward but it was nothing other than a beautiful but empty field on a hill. We could see the countryside all around and at night the lamps of Washington and civilization gleamed prettily off in the distance. It seemed to me and Will the army threw us straight into living like real soldiers whether we were ready or not.

We commenced to building our camp which the officers laid out on a grid plan so that it had little streets for each company's tents. A long wagon train pulled in at noon carrying our heavier regimental gear and we were given canvas tents to erect. Thankfully a great number of cooks came along with the wagons and they set up a commissary area as a kitchen. This was a considerable relief to us as us boys were the sort of age that we were hungry most all the time.

By the time a couple of days had passed by we had established what amounted to a perfect little town to call home. We were eating regular and drilling to learn how to arrange ourselves for battle in proper formations. My five friends and I crammed into one large A-shaped tent[4] which suited us just fine. We agreed we would do what it took to stay together for the duration of the war.

1. Railroad Depot

Railroads were a relatively new invention at the beginning of the Civil War, having been first introduced in England in 1825. Steam locomotion and the rail beds that could carry the incredibly heavy weight of the engines and loaded cars were emerging technologies that were changing the character of warfare. The Civil War in America is considered by historians to be the first modern war because of the introduction of so many crucial new inventions, like the first use of mass transit by rail, ironclad warships, submarines, naval mines, torpedoes, rifled long-range guns, surveillance balloons, gatling machine guns, and the ambulance corps.

In 1862, when Rufus got on the train in Elmira, he was traveling to the epicenter of the war along a railway line built by a private investor, which had previously been used to transport commercial products and civilians. Now the national government hired the trains to transport soldiers and supplies to the armies, something that had never been done before, enabling men and equipment to be moved en masse and relatively quickly. At first, the railroad owners charged the government outrageous fees until President Lincoln grew tired of their mercenary behavior. In January of 1862, The Railways and Telegraph Act was passed giving the Union government the right to nationalize any railroad or telegraph service it deemed necessary. Most of the owners soon fell into more generous moods rather than have their properties confiscated.

There were 19 million miles of track in the US at the beginning of the war but only one third of those were in the South. Since most of the fighting in the war was done in southern territory, the eventual damage to the rebel rail systems was far worse than damage in the North. The South also had only one manufacturing plant, in Richmond, Virginia, that could make steel rails. Eventually that plant was taken over to build armaments and then the South could neither make nor mend rail.

By 1863, Union soldiers took to ripping up lengths of track in the South, building the wooden ties into huge stacks upon which they laid the steel rails. Lighting the wood created a towering pyre which heated the rails to red hot in the middle. Then the soldiers took the rails off the pyres and literally wrapped the softened metal around trees, knowing that the rebels did not have a way of reclaiming them. The soldier's called these twisted rails "Sherman's Bowties" after the Union General

Sherman who marched from Atlanta to the sea in 1864, leaving a wide path of destruction and many twisted rails in his wake.

2. The Long Bridge

The Long Bridge was an amazing piece of wartime engineering and it made for a dramatic entrance into the theater of war. The structure was over a mile in length. Most of it was built of wood, with a quarter mile section in the middle made of masonry. At each end there was a draw bridge which was raised every night so that no dangerous rebel infiltrators could use the Long Bridge to sneak into Washington under cover of darkness. When Rufus crossed it, he knew full well that he was leaving the safety of the relatively peaceful Northern states behind.

Once the regiment was across the Potomac, they found themselves in the countryside of North Virginia, an area that had already been fought over and looked the worse for it. North Virginia had voted to secede from the Union in 1861, but the federal government in Washington could not let the territory just across the river from Washington remain in enemy hands. Federal troops seized and occupied most of the state, including the city of Alexandria which lay in sight of the capitol just down river. It was held under martial law for the duration of the war.

3. Arlington Heights

The 107th NY were four miles away from the city of Washington and now attached to its ring of defenses. Eventually the forts and other defensive structures would run thirty-three miles around the city.

4. A-Shaped Tents

Tents were not carried by individual men as a rule, though later in the war, when out on lengthy maneuvers, a man might carry a square piece of canvas that could be joined to another man's square to make a large enough piece to drape over a couple of rifles, creating a tiny pup tent for two. But usually the tents were carried by the enormous wagon trains of supplies that accompanied a Civil War army wherever it went. A foot soldier could not carry more than eighty pounds of gear and ammunition himself and still make good time on a march. The supply trains, manned by teamsters and drawn by horse and mule, brought along everything else the army needed to function as a fighting machine. There were several kinds of tents in use 1862. The biggest and by far the most elegant looking from the outside was the Sibley tent. This was a large cone of canvas, like a tepee. It was designed to house twelve men at a time. Unfortunately the army crammed as many as twenty men into a Sibley, turning them into hot, stinking caverns that the soldiers soon learned to despise. They were difficult to put up as well as heavy and cumbersome, even for the wagons to carry, and became less popular as the war went on.

The most common tents in use were all variations on simple A-frame designs. From the lowly Pup tent, the next step up was its grown up version called the Dog tent. Also known as a Wedge tent, this was a larger piece of canvas strung over a ridge pole supported by upright posts at either end with flaps that could be folded over one or both ends to keep out the weather. Four to six men were assigned to each tent. In the winter, the men foraged for wood, built short log walls cabin-style and perched their canvas tents on top of the walls to create small but efficient huts which could then be heated with a little fireplace or even a wood-burning stove if one could be obtained.

The officer's tents were bigger A-frames with two foot vertical canvas walls around the sides that made it possible to stand up, walk around, and even have meetings with other officers in relative comfort. They came in several sizes, depending on the rank of the officer, and were called simply Wall tents.

Union Troops crossing the Long Bridge

Civil War Tents

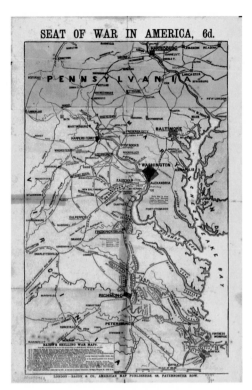

Sketches of the Seat of War

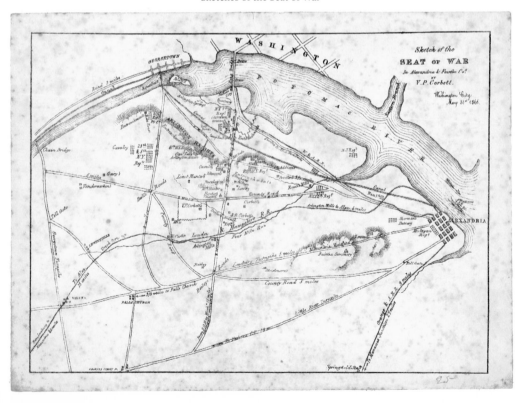

Chapter 4   Soldiers In Camp

Although we worked hard and drilled constantly[1] at Camp Seward, I found soldiering so far was agreeing with me for I was putting on weight to make up for what I had lost to the two step back at the armory. Now that we were settled and most of the boys still had some money in their pockets, a good many took to their wayward ways again with renewed energy. Our Wiggins of course, foremost among them.

Whenever possible he shirked his duties with some excuse or other and found himself a game of cards. He was encouraged along these lines by the other players who found that he was an accomplished story teller and so distracted himself that he frequently lost what little money he had in their games. I despaired that he would ever be able to send a penny home to his poor wife Mary.

At that time, Chaplain Crane wasn't able to organize any religious services for the care of our souls. I began to sorely miss spiritual guidance and took to spending some time each day in my own prayers and writing letters to my family and friends back home.

During drill practice of the fourth day in camp, the officers handed out our weapons[2] so I thought for sure we could begin to learn to handle them. I got a smooth bore while a few in the company, those who had used rifles before most likely, were issued the new rifled bores, called Springfields after the factory that built them up in Massachusetts. I received a bayonet too but no ammunition[3]. I thought for sure to get some practice in loading and firing my rifle but all we did was drill, drill, and drill some more. At least now we drilled with our rifles on our shoulders.

This is what a typical day in camp went like:

We awoke at dawn to the bugle notes of revelee, then any who were unwell lined up at our doctor's tent for sick call. His name was Doctor Flood and his grown doctor son was there with him to lend a hand, so we had two Dr. Floods to attend us.

Then we drilled. At seven am we breakfasted followed by a short time where they changed the twenty-four hour regimental guard. If we weren't assigned away to guard duty, we drilled till dinner time at noon. For most of the afternoon we worked at camp chores, hauling wood and water, building watch towers or roads, cleaning equipment & such.

At five we returned to drill practice for the hours until supper. Sundown brought a parade during which we demonstrated our new-learnt drilling skills for the higher up officers. At nine-thirty they blew the tattoo bugle to tell us to prepare for bed, and at ten came the last call, known as taps, which signified bedtime, all candles to be put out.

Eight days after we set up this first camp, forty rounds of ammunition were issued to each man and orders to move at six the next morning to a place called Fort Lyons[4] along the Arlington Heights somewhere nearby.

You can imagine then the grumbling when they marched us out on a hard walk for twelve miles with now eighty pounds of equipment on our backs, for the ammunition was very heavy. We trudged into the countryside and then trudged back to just outside the walls of Fort Lyons with only one rest and it being an awful hot day. The officers seemed to be in a state of excitement but they didn't share with us the source of our upheaval. Nothing came of our mysterious and withering march, nor was it ever explained.

When we reached our new campsite around noon, it stretched out before us, another completely empty field, this time high above the town of Alexandria and the Potomac River.

This is when I began to think soldiering was tougher than I had previously thought. And we hadn't even been to the fight tho coming through the Virginia countryside I saw houses all riddled with bullets and cannonballs & such. These sights caused the vividness of the destructive effects of war to become more real to me for I had not thoughten before on how regular folks lost their buildings and farms. Even the many kept animals we had seen on our march vanished as we passed through the areas of torn up countryside.

On that march, we also came through the city of Alexandria. I was able to personally go into the famous Marshall House for a moment. It come good to see the stars and stripes flying above the house instead of the rebel palmetto flag[5], as this was where Colonel Ellsworth the noble hero and friend to Old Abe was shot, the first patriot to die for our cause in 1861. The story was that Old Abe looked out the window of his office in Washington through his field glasses, and saw plain as day the reb flag hoisted flagrantly above a tall brick building across the river. His dear friend Ellsworth determined to go get it and remove the thorn in the side of his beloved President.

Even though the town of Alexandria was full of southern sympathizers and traitors, the brave Ellsworth made his way with a band of soldiers. They got the offending flag down off the roof and replaced it with Old Glory, but Ellsworth was shot dead descending the stairs by the landlord of the place. A great tragedy for Old Abe as Ellsworth was a good fellow and close confidante.

After our long and fruitless march, we began again to make our camp as before. Fort Lyons mounted about one hundred guns, with thirty of them monstrous things that soared above the fort walls guarding Washington and keeping the Potomac free of rebel ships. Decature guessed we were now assigned to be part of the ring of forts and encampments that made up the defenses of Washington. It was said the President had a terrible loathing of the rebs getting through to the capital city.

We were encamped outside the walls of the fort in what, I had to admit, turned out to be a splendid place, with a view of the country for miles around. We could see Washington across the bay, also Alexandria, Fairfax Courthouse, and Fort Ellsworth were about a mile distant, all in plain sight.

During the day we could look down into the city of Alexandria. You would think it was a splendid place too at first until you went down into it, then you would find it was the dirtiest hole you'd ever seen. It was an actual fact that the South was one hundred years behind the North in terms of civilization. I had heard of this before but now saw it with my own eyes. The buildings were crude, the roads nothing but ruts running about the ramshackle town, the citizens down there uneducated and very rough in their ways.

There were steamers running constantly on the river half a mile from us, loaded with our troops. They landed in Alexandria and then took the rail cars down by us before heading out to reinforce our General Pope on the Peninsula. Many of them stopped off in the city and had a drink or two. There were so many troops that if you went down there, the first you knew some drunken soldiers would pitch into you with a fight in mind. There was quarreling and fighting going on all the while and many women of sin there I am pretty certain. One day there were six or eight soldiers shot along with some negro laborers.

I couldn't get much information about the state of the war, even from Wilkerson or Colonel Diven. It was awful hard to find out what was happening or where we stood. Diven only said he thought we would see fighting in three weeks or maybe we never would. We boys took to writing home as often as we had pen and paper to ask for news or even a newspaper sent all the way from home.

I began to get very homesick and miss my family, especially my little sister Augustas. I got so sick of the sight of only soldiers that I begged my father to get her likeness put down on a photographic plate and sent to me so that it might comfort me. The folks at home probably had no idea how it made us feel to get a letter or a paper from them.

As soon as we finished building our new camp at Fort Lyon, they sent us out with axes to start chopping down the woods for the many miles of defenses that were being built up around Washington. They told us we would get forty cents extra a day for cutting down trees but since we had not been paid any wages it made no difference to the sorry state of my empty pockets.

Our worst problem in those days at Fort Lyons was the water. It turned out to be no good up there on the Heights. Wiggins thought Southern sympathizers had snuck up and poisoned it because we all got the dysentery very badly again. We had to keep everything guarded, every spring and everything else they could poison. I started to lose weight again and feel pretty poorly.

Around that time, we new volunteers began to take a close interest in the stream of soldiers we saw coming off the steamers. They sure looked tough. Their uniforms were faded and ripped up so bad we couldn't tell the officers from the enlisted men. They had mostly all lost their regulation hats and wore any old straw thing like a farm boy would pick up. I saw that their swords were rusty and their equipment mostly broken. It was no wonder to me after that that their habits had grown so poor and lowly. They were tired out from hard use was what we made it out to be.

Also we seen many of the wounded coming back from the front. They arrived on the steamers or by rail and there were a lot of them coming through every day. They were carried along on stretchers and in wagons, or just came limping and dragging themselves back to the hospitals that were said to be springing up all over Washington city. It was a sad sight and though we did not speak of it to each other, I know it gave us boys feelings of apprehension and worry.

Finally something happened, if you could call it that. They ordered us back to our old camp at Seward to build more defenses and cut down more trees, and so the month of August came to a quiet end for us, the hopeful heroes of the 107th NY Volunteers.

∞

1. Drilling

At first Rufus was simply taught how to march in step with the other members of his company, face right or left, reverse direction, and move as a unit, with prescribed distances maintained between one man and the next. Then it got more complicated as they began to learn how to organize themselves into the different formations for marching, parade, and battle.

A regiment on the move in marching or parade formation would walk as a unit with four or more men across the front. Neat, orderly columns extended behind each man along the road. In 'battle lines' the men of a regiment took up positions abreast of each other in a wide, double deep line of men, shoulder to shoulder and advancing in lock step. Or several companies might be sent ahead or to the side in a 'skirmish line' where the men took places farther apart from each other, usually to act as first responders to the enemy for the denser battle lines behind them.

Attacks were conducted in coordinated waves, with single regiments or brigades of three or four regiments advancing in their battle lines with anywhere from 25 to 300 yards between the regiments. The shorter distances between lines were much more dangerous as these gave the soldiers almost no room to maneuver once the shooting started. Though the second battle line was relatively safe from enemy musketry fire from the front, if an incoming shell from a cannon missed the men in the first line, it would most likely come down right in the midst of the second.

To shift from a marching formation into a battle formation with the least possible delay and confusion was difficult to execute in a coordinated fashion. And, it was one thing to complete these moves in a quiet open field but quite another in a small road or over broken ground, let alone under fire with the din of battle drowning out the officers' directions and smoke obstructing everyone's view of each other. It all had to be practiced over and over until it was second nature for a regiment to follow the calls for the various formations. Sometimes the orders were only conveyed to them by means of drummed signals which were the only forms of communication that would carry over the roar of cannons and musket fire.

2. Weapons

In the days before the Civil War, a charge of gunpowder, a piece of wadding, and then a round lead ball were simply rammed down a smoothly bored out metal gun barrel. When the powder was ignited by a spark from a hammer striking a flintlock at the base of the tube, the projectile was ejected from the smooth tube at considerable force.

These guns were aptly called 'smooth-bores' and were the guns that most young men in the pre-war United States had grown up using to hunt. They were extremely inaccurate and were only effective at ranges of 50 to 100 yards. This had made it necessary in the past for armies of men to run straight up close to each other so as to get near enough to inflict damage upon each other with their guns, swords, and bayonets.

During the the decade previous to the Civil War, gun manufacturers had discovered that if the gun barrel had ridges etched on the inside surface of the tube in a spiral, traveling up the length of the tube, a process called 'rifling,' the bullet would be driven rotationally up the barrel and spin through the air like a well-thrown football. It could go much farther and sustain considerable accuracy along its flight path.

A standard issue Springfield rifle was made in a factory in Springfield Massachusetts. The gun barrel was 37 inches long and it weighed 9 pounds. A well-trained soldier with a good eye could fire three rounds in a minute and hit things two to three hundred yards away, easily double the range of a smoothbore musket. A rifled gun fired one lead bullet at a time and then needed reloading using a ramrod. A percussive cap was loaded first, behind the bullet.

3. Ammunition

Not only were the rifles new during the Civil War, so was the ammunition. There had been several recent breakthroughs in the design of bullets. In the past, the round, solid lead balls of old had to be forced down the barrel of a gun on top of a charge of gunpowder. Since the balls were not a tight fit in the barrel, they had to be jammed in with a piece of paper wadding to form a seal. After firing several rounds, a soldier had to clean gunpowder and burnt debris out of the barrel or the next round would jam. This made for a slow rate of fire. The new rifled guns needed a self-cleaning projectile that still had a way of forming a seal in the barrel in front of the gunpowder. Beginning in France and then perfected at the Springfield armory in the United States, the Minie ball was designed to address these problems of jamming and rate of fire. The solution was both simple and brilliant. It began with a cone shaped piece of soft lead with circular grooves around its base. The base was concave and was embedded with a small piece of iron. When the powder charge was ignited behind it, the force of the blast pushed the bit of iron farther into the base where it expanded the soft lead base and pushed the circular grooves out to where they engaged the spiral rifling on the inside of the gun barrel, creating the necessary seal. Then the bullet spun up the length of the barrel and began its flight, not tumbling end over end but point first. As it spun through the barrel it cleaned the gunpowder residue from the previous round from the rifled ridges. The gun could be repeatedly reloaded and fired, at least until a soldier ran out of ammunition. Unfortunately for Civil War combatants, the soft Minie ball spread out and splattered on impact. If it hit an extremity it shattered bones. Then the shards of bones, as well as the pieces of flattened lead, skin, and uniform material were driven further into the body, cutting arteries, destroying tissue, and carrying bacteria deep into the wound. The surgeons of the time had neither the knowledge, instruments, nor skills to reconstruct parts of the body that had been ravaged by the deadly Minie ball. If a soldier took a direct hit to his head, torso, or stomach, it was widely considered by both doctors and soldiers to be a fatal wound. The devastating Minie ball injuries to extremities were responsible for the large number of amputations done during the war, estimated to be 60,000 in number.

4. Fort Lyons and Alexandria

The enormous Fort Lyons was built during the first year of the war and named after a general who had been killed in battle. It covered 9 acres of land and sat just to the south of Alexandria on high ground.

5. The Palmetto Flags

The first Confederate flags were called the Palmetto for the palm tree emblems in their center. Eventually they were replaced with the flag of the Army of Northern Virginia, first issued in November, 1861. It became most commonly associated with the Confederacy although there were many variations.

Life in Camp by Winslow Homer

Fort Lyon, 26th New York Infantry drilling practice

Company Kitchen

Drill

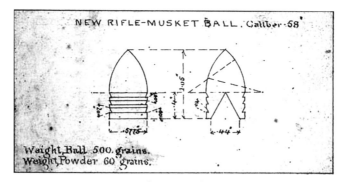

The Minie Ball

SMALL ARMS

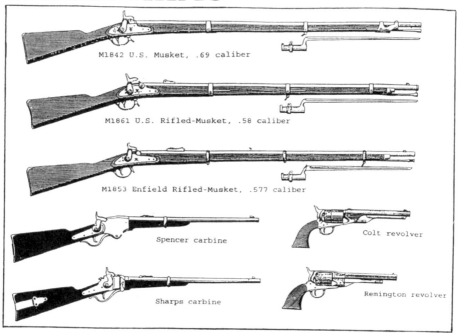

M1842 U.S. Musket, .69 caliber

M1861 U.S. Rifled-Musket, .58 caliber

M1853 Enfield Rifled-Musket, .577 caliber

Spencer carbine

Colt revolver

Sharps carbine

Remington revolver

Rifles used in Battle

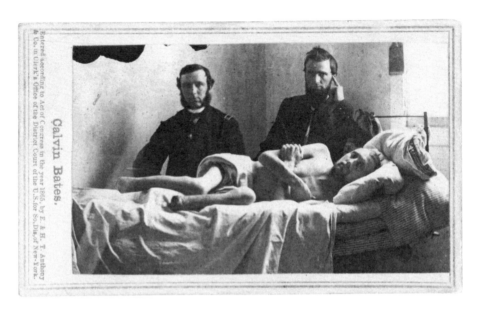

Results of Amputation

Ready to Amputate

The Marshall House - Alexandria, Virginia

DEATH OF COL. ELLSWORTH,

after hauling down the rebel flag, at the taking of Alexandria, Va. Mar 24th 1861.

Death of Col. Ellsworth

Chapter 5　　Bound for Sharpsville

The first week of September passed by calmly enough. I was getting better and better at using an ax but had made no progress at all toward learning anything about my rifle. I had never loaded it, fired it, nor seen how good or bad it aimed. The old smooth bores weren't useful for much more than firing at stationary things like barns and lazy bears & such, unless you knew exactly how far they pulled and what crazy way your bullet might travel. These things you learnt from experience with your gun in particular. You had to be up pretty close to your object to do any damage to speak of.

Tenbrook and Decature had the new rifled guns. Now, we knew those guns would shoot straight and far if they ever got a chance to shoot one of them but things did not look promising. I thought the lack of preparation meant that we new recruits weren't expected to fight anytime soon.

Then all at once, on the 6th of September, the nature of things changed very suddenly.

The 107th was assigned away to the mighty 12th Corps under the command of a General named Alpheus Williams[1]. We learnt he was a brave and humble fellow who took the side of his soldiers over polishing his own reputation. Captain Wilkerson told me he judged our new general to be of the top rail and us lucky to be put into his ranks.

We also heard we were going to directly march off northwesterly into Maryland State where the reb army was expected to try to invade the North at any minute.

I read in a newspaper we got a hold of that President Lincoln was played out with losing battles to the clever new Rebel General called Robert E. Lee and his army of mostly shoeless southern boys. Abe said that if his generals couldn't outwit the rebs then Union forces must just plain outnumber the rebs and win by overwhelming them.

So old Abe had decided to amass us all together into a new huge army of fighting men under our own new head man, General George McClellan[2]. We were to whip the rebs in one big battle on ground of Mac's choosing if possible.

The morning of the 6th Colonel Diven ordered us to leave our tents, knapsacks, and personal belongings behind in piles at our company encampment. We was to strip down for quick travel. Only things left for me to carry were a blanket, haversack, canteen, gun and ammunition so the load was considerably lighter. We fell in and began to make our way along the road.

The boys were so thrilled to be finally doing something that we broke out in singing[3] "The Battle Hymn of the Republic" as we marched. The sounds of song, of tramping feet and horses hooves, of our arms clinking and rattling caused our hearts to race along with our feet and we fairly flew down that road in the first forced march[4] of our lives. Our ranks were full, our clothes clean, and our officers all accounted for.

It turned out to be a day so sunny and hot that our clothes were soon wet through with sweat, the dust sticking to our faces and even obscuring the blue of our uniforms. For three days we marched like men possessed, the fast pace taking its steady toll on our bodies. Men fell out along the way from the effects of sunstroke and were left behind by the side of the road, slumped down and sick to death.

Soon we joined up with other regiments until we compromised a piece of a brigade under the command of a General named Gordon in what was to be our new home, the 1st Division of the 12th Corps. This, the 1st Division, ultimately held eleven regiments in all, five of which were green recruits like ourselves and the others toughened veterans of a year's worth of fights and hard marches. They sure laughed at us new boys, what they called "fresh fish," but they showed us a good deal about how to get along too, sleeping without tents and making cold coffee in our canteens, for there was little opportunity to make hot coffee or raise a shelter when it rained.

Each of us felt the rising sense of urgency the officers displayed. We were pushed along so fast that all we had time to eat was raw beef and raw pork with our hard tacks. We went on and on, not knowing where we were going to, over mountains and through valleys, and wading creeks. Old regiments said they were astonished to see us march so.

Finally one day came when we could hear the constant booming of cannon. My heart pounded in my chest for it was a mighty roar that rolled toward us over the hills. We marched right towards it until we came within far off sight of the smoke from the fighting near the city of Frederick. We stopped and stayed a short time, one day, I think. We had just missed that engagement.

We then marched closer by a place called South Mountain[5] where there was a sharp fight which our boys had won the day before. We tramped right over the field of battle and saw a great many dead rebs and yanks still laying there. It was the first time us green boys seen so many killed and it wrung at our hearts to see them left out on the ground like that. Most of them boys no older than ourselves. Their wounds gaped, bones showed through, blood turned black with flies, but there was no time given to slow down and lend a hand to bury them. In the fearsome heat the bodies lay rolled over by the bloating of their innards so that legs and arms splayed, forced apart by gases. Glazed eyes stared at the cloudless sky, mouthed sagged open. That first encounter with the awful fruits of war pitched me head first into a mood of horror I was utterly unprepared for. For how could one prepare?

The air blowing off the field was already heavy with a fetid smell I came to know too well. I imagined I saw sickly yellow tendrils of it reaching across the torn ground, seeping from the bodies in long fingers that crawled up my legs, twined around my torso, and finally crept up my face into my nostrils. Then vine like it went down my throat to give a pull as tho I was being tugged by my own innards toward the edge of a black abyss into which those dead men had so recently fallen. I noticed that even Tenbrook, who by now we all thought was going to be the best soldier out of our whole entire company, was shaken and sobered by the sights. I grabbed his arm for support as we passed by that sad display. Many of us in our regiment gagged and wretched at this our first contact with the dead. A few fell to their knees and wept. There were no songs we could think of to sing for our spirits. We marched on in stoney silence.

I counted ten days we were on that hard march before we reached a place they called Sharpsburg in the countryside of Maryland. There were rivers of men in blue pouring down through the hills and filling the roads all the while. Gradually the horror of South Mountain ebbed from my mind and was replaced once again by the high excitement of coming together with the huge gathering army that I didn't think could be defeated.

On the way, I personally saw General McClellan and a great many of the major generals on their fine horses. McClellan was called "Little Mac" by the boys on account of he was very short in stature. He, with his staff, came riding like the wind and went straight through our lines and I came close to being run down by the great man himself.

The next thing we knew we were ordered to stop and sit stock still in a field by the road throughout another long hot day. Wilkerson instructed us to clean and prepare all our equipment with great care while we waited. My friends and I could tell the battle was close at hand from the evidence we'd seen along the march. Wiggins announced he thought we were in for a "hell of a fight."

It made for a strange mix of emotions to sit still in the sun along with peaceful breezes blowing amidst the company of thousands and thousands of others, and know that any moment a great drama was to unfold that might snuff out our lives. The time dragged by slowly, hour by quiet hour.

Night came at last and we were ordered to get up and move along in the darkness without making a sound as best we could to lay down in another field, this one comprised of a crop of the sweetest smelling clover I ever encountered. The scent enveloped me in a soft cloud that for a time obscured the mounting danger of our situation.

After midnight, a light rain began to fall. I rolled across my rifle and caps to keep them dry. Officers walked constantly amongst us, reminding us to stay silent. No fires could be lit nor voices raised above even a whisper. Then before dawn the first shooting started up by our side in the woods. It must have been the lookouts and guards in the picket lines[6] exchanging gunfire, the big armies telling each other where they were positioned in the sharp language of rifles. The constant outbursts echoed over our heads and we lay ready to jump at a moment's notice. My friends and I lay close and murmured restlessly to each other of what we thought was happening out in the night. As usual, we boys hadn't one word from the officers about what we could expect to be called upon to do in the morning. I couldn't have slept a wink even if I'd wanted to.

1. General Alpheus Williams and Stonewall Jackson

Rufus's new commander, General Williams, was of a different stamp than most of the other generals. He had not been educated at West Point and so was not part of the brotherhood of officers who came from there. He also refused to do the kind of social climbing and name making for himself that officers and politicians were expected to do if they wanted their own star to rise. Rufus called this kind of behavior, 'sucking' and the men who indulged in it, 'suckers.'

Though Williams never received much acclaim during his lifetime, he was an accomplished practitioner of many professions, including lawyer, journalist, and congressman, in addition to first rate Civil War commander. After the war, he wrote an excellent and popular book called "From the Cannon's Mouth. The Civil War Letters of Alpheus Williams."

He eventually became a congressman and served in Washington for his home state of Connecticut until 1878 when he had a stroke in the Capitol building and died where he fell, an intelligent and conscientious man to the end of his days.

It was during the 12th Corps march through Maryland on the way to join up with Rufus and the other new recruits coming from Washington, that several of General William's veteran soldiers famously stumbled upon General Lee's lost SPECIAL ORDER 191.

The story of the lost order is one of those odd tales that seems stranger than fiction.

Robert E. Lee had planned his incursion into Maryland carefully, choosing hilly ground just outside the town of Sharpsburg, Maryland. He had wisely made preparations both for success and defeat, intending to give himself ways to advance if possible and retreat if necessary. In doing so he had decided on a risky and unusual series of steps to throw the huge Union army and its cautious commander McClellan off balance. Lee had to do something ingenious as he had only half as many men as the federals.

Several days before the showdown, called The Battle of Antietam, fought on Wednesday, September 17th, Lee sent General Stonewall Jackson and 14,500 men to the Union supply depot 15 miles away, at a place called Harpers Ferry. His orders to Stonewall were to capture the depot and not only seize all the arms there but destroy the rail lines that supplied the Union army. Then Stonewall was to rush back to rejoin the main rebel force before the big battle. It was a daring thing to do and absolutely dependent on speed and secrecy, for if the Union commanders got wind of such a weakening of the rebel forces gathering at Sharpsburg, they would surely attack right away and most likely destroy Lee's remaining army entirely.

General Thomas Stonewall Jackson was the man for this difficult assignment. He was Lee's most trusted officer, the commander of his whole left flank, and capable of bold, imaginative moves in his own right. He had distinguished himself and gotten his nickname a year earlier during a battle where he and his troops provided reinforcement to a line of men that was beginning to give way. It was said that he stood his ground like a 'stonewall' for others to rally behind. After that his brigade was known as the Stonewall Brigade and he was the famous Stonewall Jackson.

He originally came from Virginia and like so many of the other generals was educated at West Point. He was known for his extraordinary discipline, his religious piety, his kindness, and his tactical brilliance.

Jackson's childhood was fraught with the early death of his father and several siblings. Extreme poverty and an ailing mother added up to nearly impossible odds for a young child to overcome. When his mother remarried a man who fiercely rejected her three surviving children from the previous marriage, Jackson and a sister were sent to live with an uncle who owned a grist mill and large farm called Jackson's Mill. It was there, on the West Fork River in Virginia, that he found, for a time, a stable home life.

When his mother died several years later, an aunt took him away from the Mill but he suffered terrible verbal abuse in her household at the hands of her husband, and after a year, ran away, trekking alone at age eleven through eighteen miles of wilderness to get back to the place he loved on the river. He was able to stay there for the next seven years. Though he did farm work for his uncle most of the time and received very little formal education, he managed to teach himself to read. By age 18, he had educated himself well enough to gain acceptance to West Point.

Because of his lack of formal education, he began his West Point career at the very bottom of his class, but the relentless power of his personal discipline and determination emerged over the next four years. He worked his way up to graduate 17th out of 59 students in his class. The observation by his teachers was that if he had had one more year to catch up, he would have graduated in first place.

It must have taken a remarkable spirit to survive such a childhood, let alone become the second most famous general of the Confederacy. He seemed to have developed an unshakeable ability to achieve his goals in the face of circumstances that would have defeated a man of lesser spirit, a quality that served him and his men very well in the stressful environment of the rebellion. It was said that his troops never once gave up or retreated. General Lee knew that if anyone could ransack Harpers Ferry and get back to Antietam in time, it was surely Stonewall Jackson.

Lee sent five couriers out to his various commanders, each with a handwritten copy of 'Special Order 191' explaining the risky plan to divide his army and send Stonewall on his secret mission.

Several days later on Sept. 13, two Union 12th Corps soldiers came through a campsite previously used by rebel troops. One of the men, seeing several cigars wrapped in a bit of paper near the remains of a fire pit, picked them up and found to his astonishment that the paper was in fact, Lee's Special Order 191, apparently dropped by one of the couriers. The lost dispatch was immediately relayed to General Williams and then up the chain of command to General McClellan himself.

For a brief time, Mac had the opportunity to act quickly and inflict fatal damage on Lee's divided forces but he didn't use the opening to move decisively. He was convinced that Lee still had over 100,000 men at his disposal and thought the lost dispatch might be a trap. Soon General Lee found out through his extensive network of spies that Mac knew about the plan.

Lee then sent orders to Jackson to race home as soon as he had taken Harpers Ferry, which he did, arriving just in time to reinforce the rest of the Confederate army on the 17th at the battle and help fight the big Union army to a standstill.

2. General George McClellan

In September of 1862, President Lincoln said he was "greatly distressed" to have no better option for commander of the Northern

Armies than General McClellan who was by all assessments and track record not a very good tactician in battle. What McClellan did have going for him was that he was a skilled organizer. Lincoln thought that McClellan could at least get a very large number of men into proper shape for battle. Then perhaps the Union would at last have the advantage of out-numbering the rebels that Lincoln had foreseen in June, even if they could not out-general them. So, Lincoln crossed his fingers and instructed McClellan to take over the Union army's high command. Known simply as 'Mac' or 'Little Mac' due to his short stature (he was only 5'4") McClellan was one of the human puzzles of the Civil War. Also educated at West Point, he was bright, ambitious, and extremely popular with the men for his stylish flare and warm affection for them. But he was a flawed commander and a man who did not seem capable of learning from his mistakes. He made the same ones over and over, boisterously defending his actions and blaming others for his failures all the while.

He did have exceptional skill in one capacity and that was in the training of an army.

Lincoln said of him, "If he can't fight himself, he excels in making others ready to fight." However, once Mac was faced with deploying his well-trained men upon the field, his flaws and fears kicked in. He regularly overestimated the strength of his enemy and seemed reluctant to move his men quickly or even in a well coordinated manner, which proved disastrous on the fast and ever-changing stage of a major battlefield. He also never pursued an advantage but hung back mired in caution and indecision. At the bottom of all these hesitations seemed to be a need to be guaranteed that anything he did would have a good outcome, something that is simply impossible to know ahead of time in war.

When the New Army of the Potomac was put into Mac's hands, it amounted to as many as 85,000 men by the eve of the battle at Antietam.

Mac could not get beyond his cautious nature and though he was given command of this large number of men, he harbored the conviction that Lee's army outnumbered his own by as much as two to one. Lee, most likely, had quite a bit to do with Mac's impression of superior forces on the rebel side, for Lee, knowing full well Mac's tendencies, had had his spies and infiltrators spread false information behind Union lines. Psychological warfare was alive and well during the Civil War, in use especially by the rebel generals who knew that they were the underdogs in the contest.

Mac would go on to fight the up-coming battle at Antietam without using one quarter of his army. He held 1 and 1/2 out of 6 Corps in reserve as insurance against the imagined hordes of rebels hidden somewhere in the hills of Maryland, thereby doing exactly the opposite of what Lincoln had in mind, and probably doing exactly as Lee had hoped. After the Battle of Antietam, Lincoln thought better of the appointment of Mac and eventually removed him from high command. Mac then became a thorn in Lincoln's side and ended up running against him in the presidential election of 1864. Mac lost the election but he continued to avidly undermine Lincoln and further defend himself against the many critics of his actions during the Campaign at Antietam.

3. Singing

Music was as important in military life to the soldiers during the Civil War as was religion. It provided a necessary morale booster and outlet for the members of both armies, cutting across cultural, economic, religious, and even racial differences. Each regiment had its own brass band and drums to accompany them on formal occasions but it was not uncommon to hear songs raised spontaneously in several locations among a regiment's tents or work parties.

The men of both armies sang "Glory Hallelujah," "The Battle Cry of Freedom" and a wide assortment of songs providing themselves with entertainment and esprit de corps, as well as with a way to express their homesickness and fears about future events.

General Lee once famously remarked,"I don't believe we can have an army without music."

Many soldiers brought instruments along with them into service. Life in the armies included singing and playing music in camp, singing on the march, and even singing as one went into battle. In their time off, in addition to playing music and singing, there was a lot of dancing done.

4. Forced March

A forced march was when the army was made to move at a much faster pace on foot than normal, a pace that would tire them out as it was said 'excessively.' It was only used in the case of a military emergency because at the end of such a grueling march, the infantry would need a period of recuperation before they were able to fight effectively. This forced marching was something the commanders only asked of their troops when they had no other choice.

5. South Mountain

Fought September 14th, 1862. To meet the challenge of Robert E. Lee's invasion of Maryland, General McClellan marched his army very fast to three passes in the South Mountain range. This range is the northern most portion of the Blue Ridge Mountains. There were intense engagements at the three gaps. Federal troops finally gained control of the passes but the rebels fought so hard that Lee was able to gain the time he needed to reunite his divided army (see Lost Order 191) and get ready for the battle of Antietam outside Sharpsburg.

6. Picket Lines

A 'picket' is a word for a fence post or a stake driven into the ground. In the military, it denoted a guardian of the army itself while the army was not on the move. Pickets were an advanced protective guard, just like a fence. They were organized into squads composed of several officers and 40 soldiers, then they were posted in a strung out line beyond the regimental encampments, and tasked with watching for any signs of change in the enemy's position. It was an extremely dangerous and sometimes lonely job. If the enemy did advance, or send out its own pickets or sharpshooters, the men on picket duty were the first they encountered and therefore the first to be shot at or captured. Because it was so dangerous, picket duty was routinely rotated among the men of a regiment. When two opposing armies were as close together as they were that night at Antietam, pickets exchanged rifle fire throughout the night.

General Alpheus Williams, Rufus's favorite officer

General McClelland and Wife Mary

Pickets in the Woods

The Songs of War by Winslow Homer

Battle of Antietam

Chapter 6   Antietam

In the cold breaking dawn, Diven finally come for us. We rose stiffly from our blankets as he angrily kicked out the embers of the fires some of the boys had made. There was no breakfast for anyone to be had that fateful day. We were only given time enough to drink yesterday's coffee from our canteens before we set off marching toward the muffled booms and echoes that had commenced to roll toward us over the hills in a ghostly fashion. Rises, dips, and stands of trees began to slowly emerge from the mists of the long chilly night.

Along the way, I decided to leave my friends a short distance behind and tell Wilkerson I would volunteer to join the regimental color guard[1] for the battle. I hardly knew why I did such a thing for I understood the guard to be a very hot place in a fight with both sides endeavoring to bring down an enemy's flags the better to lend confusion and discouragement to each other's ranks. But I'd heard the guard needed more men and I figured God would do with me what ever it was he had in mind for me regardless of where I was placed in the battle. Wilkerson said alright so off I went.

When we had got into our marching formation, the Captain rode before us and shouted out that a General Hooker's 1st Corps[2] had opened the fight at daybreak about a mile northwest of our present position. We were heading out to lend what Wilkerson called support to Hooker's troops.

Before I had time to blink, we were suddenly off, hiking fast cross country over plowed land, through cornfields, and small woods, and also past the neatest little farms you could imagine. I feared for their inhabitants as much as our own troops, knowing what I now knew of the effects of war. It seemed just like a mighty thunderstorm with flooding and tornadoes was darkening the horizon, on its way to sweep us all away, soldier, citizen, and beast alike.

Soon we found ourselves marching in a road that was sunk into the land by heavy wagon use. Large stacked fences ran criss-cross down both sides, these comprised of the heaviest sort of rails. The fences impeded our progress so Diven rode by us shouting "tear them down, tear them down."

We tried but just couldn't make a job of it. The fences were too strong and anchored in the earth like stone. Diven then commanded us to climb them. We started to swarm up and over when all of a sudden the enemy must have got us in cannon range. A few shells were thrown in our direction. For the first time the 107th was under artillery fire.

Instantly the Colonel ordered us to get off the fences and start running down the road again. We needed little encouragement. The officers rode their horses fast along the ranks urging us on toward a wooded area looming up at us through the trails of fog. When we got closer we discovered there was already some skirmishing[3] going on amongst the trees. We lay down behind the fence, under what cover it could provide, awaiting further orders.

Now General Gordon came along with orders for our 107th New York and another green regiment, the 13th New Jersey, to peel off from the Division and guard a smaller stand of nearby trees. He ordered us to hold that ground at all costs.

The enemy's snipers[4] must have been hid along the tree lines far to the front of us because a smattering of bullets began to whine and ping above our heads once we had got into our new position there by the copse. Several of the boys tried to return fire but the reb snipers were too far away for the reach of our guns. The sergeant of the color guard told me those snipers had such nifty rifles they could hit targets a mile off and were also better shots than our yankee snipers as a rule.

He said, "You better be careful Rufus, my dear boy, keep yer head down or you'll cetch a bullet from them johnnies up in those there trees ahead!"

So I stayed low glancing up only when I saw and heard a most unusual sight coming our way. A large party of officers was galloping along our lines waving and hollering fit to be tied. Right out in front was the famous white haired general I had only heard tell about, the one they called Mansfield[5], head of the whole, mighty 12th Corps at the time. He had been put in charge of the Corps just a few days before and General Williams was put back in lower at 1st Division commander. Seemed like the high command danced our good Old Williams up and down the ranks like a girl at a ball.

Mansfield's white hair was blowing out behind him in the wind. He hollered "Hold your fire! Hold your fire!" and waved his hat as if he had no idea we were being shot at or of the terrible danger out there in the open from the snipers' bullets whizzing about so liberally.

Some of our boys and officers tried in vain to yell warnings to the General and his men, but he swept on by us stuck in his mind on some mistaken mission.

Some distance past me the reb snipers got him. They shot the General and his poor horse too for good measure. We saw him wobble in the saddle as the horse slowed down to a walk. He then dismounted and led his wounded mount to the shelter of a tree but once there, dropped the reins and fell to the ground in a heap. His aides were off their horses in a jiffy and running to help him. The horse, confused and bleeding from the neck, veered slowly away first toward us and then the poor beast bolted in the direction of enemy lines.

For the first time my faith in the strength of our army faltered and a chill fell across my hopes for winning this battle decisively and going home soon. Old Abe appeared to be right about our poor generalling. I had just watched our top man get shot down through his own error in judgement. I looked down the line to my friends and saw they was shaking their heads in amazement as was I and everyone.

Then Diven yelled for our medical man, Dr. Flood and his medics, to go help the General and they hopped to it on the double. After wrapping him in blankets, they carried him through our ranks to the field hospital, which we had been told was being set up at one of the farm houses we had passed by the night before.

As soon as General Mansfield was out of the fight, our first Commander, General Williams, was put back in charge of the Corps. He was apparently not one to favor us green recruits and so threw us straight into the fight. Captain Wilkerson gave out new orders to run like the dickens into the woods, flush out the snipers and get through to Hooker's men beyond.

We jumped to our feet and rushed off as ordered. The snipers must have seen the hordes of us coming because their fire melted away like magic before our advance. But new dangers took their place. As we entered the trees a big shell buzzed in and struck the boys along our line. I saw a tangle of men go down out of the corner of my eye, then heard wailing and yelling behind me.

My heart clenched at those awful sounds but we couldn't stop our drive forward. Above our heads the trees were suddenly exploding into splinters from heavy shelling and the din of battle assaulted our senses at every turn. I heard later one of the regiment's youngest boys, age sixteen, had his legs blowed off by that first shell and died in agony with no one to comfort him as his blood flowed out in a torrent onto the ground. The boys said he was crying out something terrible for his mother to bring him water with his dying breaths.

Breaking free of those dreadful woods, we threw ourselves on the ground again to take some cover and cetch our breath, being badly winded by then.

I then looked up and saw in front of us lay an enormous cornfield. Across its breadth wandered long wavering lines of grey and blue soldiers, regiments sweeping this way and that, with smoke and mist drifting along, carried off by what little wind there was. Bodies of the dead and wounded laid like small dark sticks across the ground amongst the corn which was cut down to stubs and broken stalks. It wasn't even eight in the morning but already death had reaped a cruel crop.

Our 12th Division cannon boys[6] soon arrived to unlimber their guns to the sides of us. Diven rode up once again and ordered us to throw off our coats and anything else weighing us down. We were to advance across the field toward a small white building we could barely spy through the smoke to take the place of Hooker's exhausted and retreating troops.

There was no time to dwell on any trepidations we might harbor, we just went at it, me with the color guard, my friends off at little distance, still all of us shoulder to shoulder in the lines. We ran crouching low as we could, jumping over bodies, horses, and strewn equipment, dodging shells and wincing at the awful, deadly insect sound of bullets passing by our heads too close for comfort. You could not dodge the bullets but they were not so apt to rip a man all to pieces as a shell. The shells were bigger and exploded the most of them sounding like bumblebees as they came in. One would come close to your head and whiz and then one a little farther would whiz and bang and down would go two or three men all tore up.

Whilst we advanced, what must have been what was left of Hooker's men poured back through our ranks, desperate to get out of that open slaughterhouse and beyond it to the shelter of the trees and batteries behind us.

Our company and the color guard almost made it to the white house[33] but another of the sturdy fences broke our progress. We lay down near it for cover and started to hold that position in the very center portion of the fight. We was pinned so close to the ground we could hardly squirm round to reload our guns, but we did manage to fire off shot after shot. It seemed plenty strange that we learnt more about how to shoot our guns in that blasted cornfield than we'd ever done before.

Aside from that, there were only two other thoughts in my mind, one, that I must kill as many johnnies as possible and two, that I never let even one of their infantry get through to our cannons boys behind us.

Time both stood still and stretched, impossible to tally amidst the chaos and noise.

Eventually I found my ammunition running low and about this same time I seen a couple of wounded reb boys lying on the ground nearby. I thoughten to go over and talk with them and see if I could lend a hand. It never occurred to me that just minutes before I was bent on killing those boys but now that they were fallen, their place in my thinking underwent a change, so I crawled over to them.

I said, "Well boys where are you hurt?"

The one closest to me was lying on his belly but up on his elbows, seemingly quite alert. The other lay on his back with one leg sticking out at a bad angle.

"Wahl, yank," says the first, "I got a knock on mah heep but it don't feel too awful deep. Its bleedin' bad I reckon tho."

"Okay Johnnie," I says, "Take a rag or something and put it directly on the wound and push hard. Even if it pains you something fierce it will stem that blood flow."

So, we were just beginning to discuss their situation this way in a friendly manner when 'Bang!' a fearsome pop occurred practically right above my head and that was the last thing I recall of those moments. A piece of that shell must have took me over the eye for it knocked me most crazy and I laid there senseless for some time while the battle raged around me like a great beast, devouring reason and time.

Decature later told me a shell exploded right above the color guard and he judged I would have been killed if I hadn't crawled off to talk to them reb boys. Many of my fellow guard were either killed or wounded, the sergeant among them. Our fine honorary blue silk banner that Old Abe gave us was cut to strings, our regimental flag staff broke and fallen to the ground.

My friends nor anyone could get to me where I fell. The battle continued to pound on for I know not how long until I came to, dizzy, deaf and practically blind. I remember trying to raise my blouse to my face to staunch the blood but having a hard time of it because of my haversack and belt. I pulled them off and threw them from me.

I thought the side of my face might be blowed away and the boys all thought so too because of the copious blood flowing from the wound. Tenbrook told me later he thought my nose was plumb gone. The strangest thing was I felt no pain at all. Dragging my gun, I stumbled toward the rear lines as a medic finally came out to assist me. I didn't want to leave my friends out on the field but he said I must. He walked me to the field hospital[7] where I sank down again in a daze by the farmhouse door.

When at last I got in to see an exhausted surgeon in his bloody apron, he wrapped my head with a bandage across my eye. Seems the shell fragment had caught me a good clip down one side of my face but he told me my eye was likely going to be all right. Once he had the bleeding stopped and I could walk again without excessive dizziness, it seemed to me it was getting on, perhaps late in the afternoon. Nevertheless, as the battle obviously continued, I went and found Captain Wilkerson to ask if I might go back to the fight. He said that I shouldn't take my place with the boys until I could go with both eyes on it.

Since they wouldn't let me back onto the field, I hung around the hospital and began to help out there as best I could, binding up wounds for the boys, fetching water & such things, the need being so very great.

Casualties poured in all through the rest of the day and night till there wasn't a spot on the ground that did not hold a man or what was left of one. The gore was unimaginable. In places the dirt was turned to mud from the blood. All I could do for those who were mostly beyond help was be of some comfort. All this taking place under a thick layer of terrible din from the explosions on the battlefield. It truly was a hell on earth. How is it I wondered, that men could inflict this ghastly damage on each other, how had it come to this? So contrary to the teachings of our Lord. I had thought I was doing my duty. Now I couldn't help myself from wondering, "duty to who?"

Because, imagine if you can a full country acre of space taken up with groaning, bloody men, the medics bringing in more all the while. Many of those men falling into the deepest silence of their lives for eternity. Each and every one of them someone's son, brother, or father.

Thank God, there were a lot of plain good folks that were trying to help us, even some women came out there onto the field of battle with bullets still flying, risking their lives and limbs to tend to the wounded. I was greatly affected by their bravery and thought them truly angels of mercy.

In the early morning hours, as it grew lighter, I used a borrowed pencil and a fragment of an old letter from home I had in my trouser pocket, to scribble a rough note to my father to let him know I had come through all right. When I was done, I handed it off to a citizen volunteer who said he would make sure it was stamped and got sent.

My note said:

Father I cannot write there are men dying all around me and they need my assistance. I should like to write you a long letter and will as soon as I can. This has been a terrible Battle[8] and I saw the worst of it. Our regiment was in the worst part of it and took the place of 3 regiments that run. This is all the paper I have or can get & I have no stamps. I lost everything I had in the battle. part of the time I get something to eat and part of the time I don't. Good bye. Write as soon as you get this, direct to Washington. Send me some papers if you can. If you send them to Washington, we will get them,

R Harnden

Then I went back to dressing the boys' wounds while keeping my good eye peeled for my friends. The battle was ended but I didn't know how to find out how they had faired. I was awful anxious on their behalf for who could've foreseen what our regiment had endured in that cornfield. I had no way of knowing if we had even won the fight[9]. I don't think anyone knew. We did hear that General Mansfield, shot through the abdomen, had died that morning.

1. The Color Guard

Banners and flags were extremely important to every regiment. They were carried aloft on the march and into battle. They were known as a regiment's "colors" and were its identifying markers. Held high above the mass of men, fluttering from their wooden staffs, they provided a rallying point for the soldiers in situations of confusion on the field, or revealed the position and progress of a given regiment to the commanders who watched the battles through binoculars, called field glasses, from the hills.

Each unit carried two banners, one the national colors, a 6x6 foot traditional stars and stripes with the regiment's name and number sewn into the central stripe, the other a 6.5 x 6 foot blue silk flag, trimmed in gold, bearing the United States' eagle design with the name of the regiment on a ribbon beneath the eagle's feet.

Regimental flags were carried by a small group of men aptly called the Color Guard. It was a very dangerous job as the attention of the enemy was inevitably drawn to its opponents' flags and efforts to destroy each others colors continued unabated for tactical and symbolic reasons. It was not uncommon for an entire color guard to be wiped out by one well-aimed anti-personnel shell.

2. General Hooker's 1st Corps

The Union general named 'fighting' Joe Hooker with his 1st Corps of 8,600 men, had begun the engagement at daybreak. His artillery laid down a heavy wave of shell on part of Stonewall Jackson's Division, just back from Harpers Ferry the day before. Jackson's men were hiding in a 30-acre cornfield and some woods. Hooker observed that one could just make out the shiny tips of the rebel infantry's bayonets above the sea of corn stalks and tassels.

General Hooker's many regiments, following up on the cannons' effects, were able to drive the rebels from the field and the eastern portion of the woods by around 6 am as the sun began to burn off the fog. Hooker took note of that first hour of fighting as he sat upon his horse and watched from a hillside.

"In the time I am writing, every stalk of corn in the northern and greater part of the field was cut as closely as with a knife, and the slain lay in rows precisely as they had stood in their ranks a few minutes before. It was never my fortune to witness a more bloody, dismal battlefield."

Hooker's men were in turn, subjected to a storm of shell, canister, and musket fire as they made their way into the open fields. Then all at once, 2000 rebel troops emerged from the woods on the far side of the field and, with a piercing rebel yell, unleashed a volley that cut the General's own men down. Unable to hold the ground, the 1st Union Corps turned and began to run back toward the shelter of the woods on their side with rebel infantry hard on their heels.

Mansfield's 12th Corps, though they had been called to back up the advance of Hooker's troops, were not yet in position behind them. General McClellan had seemingly not taken into account the time it would take for the 12th Corps to march cross-country to the 1st Corp's position. The Battle at Antietam would soon prove to be a travesty of badly coordinated efforts by the Union generals. The 12th Corps were over a mile away from the 1st Corp's problems when they got the order to skip breakfast and move out.

3. Skirmish Lines

Civil War armies protected themselves when not in actual battle with scouts, picket lines, and skirmishers. These were made up of men who had separated themselves from the main body of troops in order to do their jobs. Skirmish lines moved ahead or to the side of the main force in a line and would frequently engage the enemy's skirmishers in what were small fights, therefore known as skirmishes.

4. Snipers

A sniper was one of the most useful and effective weapons a general had at his disposal during the Civil War. As well as being just a good way to kill people, it was also a powerful element of psychological warfare. A sniper's job was to pick off the enemy, especially its officers. Targeting officers this way upset the command structure and struck terror into the hearts of that officer's men. A sniper did this from a distant, hidden position so that those under attack had only the vaguest idea where the bullets were coming from.

Snipers were highly trained in both the arts of marksmanship and camouflage. Each regiment would have a number of snipers attached to it. The South used them much more extensively than the North in an effort to level the playing field against the North's superior numbers of men and artillery.

Snipers used different kinds of rifles than infantrymen. Their guns were heavier, with much longer barrels and were fired from fixed positions under cover using gun rests like tree branches, fence rails, rocks, or even dead horses. These rifles in addition to being more accurate, could hit targets at ranges of 600 to 1000 yards away. The domestically produced Sharps, or English rifles like the Whitworth were preferred, hence the other name for a sniper, 'sharpshooter.' These marksmen's guns had barrel length scopes to help a sniper increase their lethal effects.

The rebel snipers who fired at the 107th NY that morning could have been a half mile away, well out of the accurate range of the regiment's standard issue guns.

5. General Mansfield

The new 12th Corps commander, General Mansfield, born in Connecticut like Williams, was a traditional career officer. He had gone to West point and then advanced slowly up the ranks during peacetime. In the 1840s he finally saw combat in the Mexican-American War, in which he distinguished himself and was wounded. He was given a citation for bravery and continued his gradual ascent to eventually become the Inspector General of the United States government.

When the Civil War broke out, he was again promoted, this time to the rank of Major General in the Union Army, but saw very little action during the first year of the war. He looked much older than his 58 years on account of his bright white hair and beard but he was energetic and demonstrated a lot of enthusiasm for his men, often riding out to personally cheer them on.

Now, two days before the battle at Antietam, he was suddenly put in command of the entire 12th Corps. Although he had 40 years of army experience under his belt, he was not comfortable with the weighty responsibility of such a high command. He knew it, his aides knew it, and General Williams knew it. They considered him to be nervous, fussy, and somewhat hard to handle, often given to debilitating bouts of anxiety when faced with big decisions.

He was especially worried about the many new recruits that had so recently joined the 12th Corps. To General Williams he expressed the view that if he were to send them into battle, they would most likely just panic and run away.

The afternoon of the 16th of September, Mansfield and the whole 12th Corps, totaling around 7200 men, arrived near Sharpsburg.

6. Batteries of Cannon

One could divide the cannons used during the war into two groups, the "field artillery" that travelled with the army and the "heavy artillery" that was relatively stationary. The huge guns at Fort Lyons were of the stationary sort.

At the beginning of the war, cannon design had not progressed much since the Napoleonic era of the past century. Even though there was a mind-numbing array of different kinds in use, all cannons were basically just like muskets only bigger. They ranged in size from the small ones that could be wheeled around on a cart up to the 100,000 pound monsters, cast from iron, brass or bronze. One end was left open and the other end was closed, with a hole in the closed end into which a fuse or piece of copper wire was inserted. A bag of gunpowder, known as the charge, was loaded into the open end and shoved back to the fuse with a ramrod, then a projectile was pushed in after that. The gun was fired by introducing fire to the powder either by lighting the fuse, or more commonly by yanking on a rope called the lanyard line that was attached to the piece of copper wire, thus creating a friction spark and causing an explosion that ejected the ammunition.

Some cannon were smoothbores and the newer ones currently being cast in the North and England were rifled.

As the war opened, both sides scrambled to find enough cannons with which to arm their entrenched positions and armies. They used whatever they could get their hands on. The existing forts of the United States Government, like Fort Lyons, were already well fortified structures when the war began, giving the Federals yet another advantage over the Confederates. There were no developed industrial resources in the South where guns could be manufactured, at least not at the start of the war. The rebels were forced to either import their cannons from England at considerable expense or better yet capture them from the North which was free, if you didn't count the loss in lives.

Although England was still officially a neutral country in regards to the American Civil War, in reality there was strong sympathy for the South, especially among the upper, most powerful classes. The English demonstrated their allegiance by illegally supplying the South with the arms it so desperately needed. Very good rifled guns and cannons were being designed and built in the English armories and the gun makers not only wanted a market for their products, they also wanted to field test them under battle conditions. The English ran the Northern marine blockades to export their wares to the Southern states, a highly dangerous but extremely profitable endeavor, most of them coming ashore off Cape Fear in North Carolina.

There were a number of different cannon projectiles in use at the time of the Civil War. The simplest was the solid round cannonball, which was not very effective except against masonry fortifications or structures, other artillery pieces, and large stationary targets, like horses. More effective projectiles included various types that exploded, either in the air or on impact. Rufus was to encounter shell, canister, and grapeshot - the primary antipersonnel cannon ammunitions.

A shell was hollow and contained another powder charge with its own detonation fuse which was timed to go off while the shell was above the heads or otherwise close to the ranks of one's enemy, bursting the shell casing into dozens of jagged pieces that hit a number of men at one time. Rufus's wound at Antietam was caused by a piece of shell casing.

Canister was by far the most damaging concoction in use. It was a tin can filled with 27 small, cast iron balls, each weighing about a half pound, that was used to great advantage against attacking infantry at close distance, turning each cannon into a very large and effective shotgun with horrible results for one's enemy. Grapeshot was frightening but less effective. It was another grouping of larger round balls, 2 inches in diameter. It did not have the scope or range of shell or canister.

Regardless of the type of ammunition in use, all of the sounds associated with cannon fire were terrible, from the initial blast of the main charge going off, to the screaming noise the projectiles made when traveling through the air at high speed and the secondary explosion or impact with the ground. It amounted to a din that was overwhelming and practically beyond description, though many a man would try, including Rufus. Aside from the more obvious injuries these projectiles inflicted, it was not uncommon for an exploding shell to so severely concuss those nearby as to render them mute or deaf in one ear, or so shocked that they joined the long lines of injured who had to be assisted from the battlefield and taken to a hospital for a lengthy period of recovery. Some in fact never recovered the full extent of their previous abilities and were said to be "shell-shocked."

The field artillery that Rufus encountered came in units called Batteries. A battery was a remarkably complicated little world of its own, set apart from the foot soldiers of the infantry. In the beginning of the war a battery was assigned to each brigade but that soon proved to be too rigid a system and by 1863, multiple batteries were placed under each division's command so that a general could coordinate their placement. Of course there were a range of differences between the combatants over where and when to place batteries of cannon, as well as constant evolution in the commander's recognition of how best to deploy their field artillery.

A battery was composed of four to six cannons, each mounted on a gun carriage. For travel, the carriage was attached behind a wagon which held a heavy ammunition chest and was drawn by a team of 6 horses, with 3 drivers riding the 3 horses on the left hand side. Behind them came another wagon called a caisson, carrying 3 more ammunition chests, also pulled by a 6 horse team. Each battery was further accompanied by a traveling forge, wagons to carry tents and supplies, and 6 more caissons of reserve ammunition, as well as extra wagons filled with food for the horses, all pulled by more horses or mules. There were a lot of horses involved in the transportation of a battery. During the battles the horses were kept standing near the cannons and ammunition wagons so that if a battery needed to move, it could do so right away. Horses were big and they were stationary, hence a high death rate among their number. An unimaginable one million horses would be killed during the course of the Civil War. If we speak of cannon fodder we might include these poor creatures in our calculations.

The gun crews usually consisted of 9 men per each cannon. They had a high chance of being injured too. Once again, the new rifled guns carried by the infantry had changed the lay of the land. Most of the field cannons were affective against foot-soldiers at distances under 300 yards, while the new rifles gave the infantry who knew how to shoot a range well over 300 yards. Artillery pieces therefore had to be placed within range of rifle fire to be effective and were at risk accordingly.

In spite of, or perhaps because of, the dangerous nature of their work, artillerymen were famous for their allegiance to fellow crew members and their branch of the service. A gun crew had to work together under pressure and in a physically demanding situation. Once a battery was moved and set up by its drivers, an activity called unlimbering, the gun crews took over and commenced the highly coordinated series of steps necessary to load and fire their weapons. When the cannon began firing, spurts of flame, explosions, and choking clouds of white smoke, as well as the unwelcome attentions of the enemy, dominated the scene.

An artillery man, grown proud of his skill, toughness, and team effort would never condescend to be a lowly enlisted man again. For someone like Rufus, and the rest of the new recruits in the 107th, to earn respect from members of the artillery service was an honor worth striving for.

7. A Small White Building

The Dunker Church was to become a famous landmark the day the Battle of Antietam was fought. It was built in 1852 by local farming families. Originally from Germany, these citizens practiced a form of Christianity that emphasized simplicity, modesty, and peace. The name 'Dunker' came from their form of baptism which included being dunked under water. Members of this church were opposed to slavery and refused military service. Their churches' architecture was totally simple without steeples or even crosses.

8. The Field Hospital

The field hospital that Rufus was in did not amount to much of a medical facility. Each regiment or division usually set up its own hospital either in an actual field or at confiscated farmhouse and its outbuildings as this was preferable to having to rig up cover for hundreds of injured men. The hospitals were staffed by the regimental surgeons, their assistants, and untrained male nurses or citizen volunteers. Many of the volunteers were women like Clara Barton or family members who came from home to take care of their loved ones.

Unfortunately, field hospitals were much more dangerous places than the actual battlefields for the average Civil War soldier. Disease, malnutrition, and infections like gangrene ran rampant among the fallen. As one Union soldier said," If a fellow has to go to the hospital you might as well say good bye to him."

There was so little knowledge of the effects of hygiene and nutrition or of how to best care for a patient in the process of recovery that many soldiers quickly succumbed to traumatic injuries and infections. The doctors did observe that vegetables and fruits seemed to promote better healing but it was extremely difficult to obtain adequate amounts of fresh food for the patients in the field hospitals. For instance, eating soon became a major problem for Rufus. He was lucky that he was ambulatory and could search for food in the countryside. Bed bound men could not go out and forage like their healthier counterparts.

Before a soldier wounded in battle got to a field hospital, he would first either walk, as Rufus had, if he were able, or be carried by the medics to a forward station. Medics went out onto the battlefield to attend casualties where they fell. They carried water, bandages, and whiskey with which to deaden pain.

They took the injured man by stretcher or accompanied him on foot to a forward station where he received more treatment. Forward stations were supposed to be equipped with water, cleaning basins, sponges, bandages, chloroform, and additional painkillers, most commonly opium. From there, the lightly injured had to walk back from the front to the larger field hospital in the rear. The badly hurt had to wait for the ambulance cart to come get them. Sometimes they waited for hours. Often wounded men, especially the losers in a fight, had to lie out in the open on the field for several days. When help finally came, it most likely came from the medics of one's enemy and with them the knowledge that if one survived one's wounds, one was headed North or South to a military prison, another potentially deadly place, teeming with diseases and other difficulties.

9. A Terrible Battle

The awful slaughter in and around the Antietam cornfield and the Dunker Church raged for 9 hours altogether on September 17th, 1862. The fighting was so intense that a sort of hysteria over took the combatants. This state was called 'Red Sky' by soldiers who lived through it, words which offer a window of understanding upon an altered state of mind that can develop in extreme warfare. Men overcome with Red Sky went quite literally insane for a time, screaming, yelling, and even laughing, having abandoned all instinct towards self preservation.

At one point after one assault had been repelled, one of Rufus's Company A reportedly jumped upon a rock, careless of the bullets that still flew around his head, and waving his hat, cried out, "Bullie! set 'em up on the other alley!" as if he was at a bowling party with his friends.

Major Colby from the 107th NY reported that by the end of the engagement, he was too weak to stand or walk, so great was the toll of the crashing cannons firing incessantly over his head. It was estimated that as many as 200 dead or wounded rebel fighters were lying near them, and several more of their own men had been killed, with many more wounded by shell fragments, some from the battery behind them when a shell had burst prematurely above their heads.

Around 2 o'clock, the exhausted 107th NY Regiment and Cothran's battery were relieved by General Williams and left the battle by way of the East Woods. By the end of the day thousands of men lay out upon the huge cornfield, many of them groaning and crying out for help and water, with thousands more casualties lying hidden in the woods. Dead and dying horses, broken equipment, and blood-soaked clothing added to the awful scene. Medics and volunteer civilian nurses tried to attend the wounded in the cornfield where they had fallen but it was still extremely dangerous, even after the major fighting had ceased. Clara Barton herself, a civilian volunteer nurse and the future founder of the American Red Cross, knelt down in the field to give a wounded man a drink of water when a bullet whizzed through her sleeve and hit the man in the chest, killing him instantly.

One of the wounded left for dead that day was a young man named Oliver Wendell Holmes, Jr. He had been shot through the neck. The medics eventually found him and brought him back to the hospital where even he expected to die from his terrible injury. He managed to scrawl out a note bearing his name and address in the event that his body needed to be identified and shipped home. Incredibly, he did survive and became a famous man. He lived to be 94 after serving on the US Supreme Court for 33 years.

The major fighting on the 17th of September shifted south of the cornfield during the afternoon to the army's center for 4 hours of terrible struggle and then to the left flank where Union General Burnside's Corps mounted an intense assault on Lee's right flank. Unfortunately for Burnside, just when it seemed he would prevail, the rest of Stonewall Jackson's men got back from Harpers Ferry in time to support the faltering rebel line. McClellan did not send in reserves to help Burnside and the day ended with another lost opportunity.

The 107th NY suffered 12 killed or mortally wounded and five captured or missing. 49 others were officially listed as wounded; Rufus was not counted at that time, perhaps because he could initially walk off the field. The total for all men put out of commission was estimated by Colonel Diven as 63. They had gone from fresh-faced recruits at dawn to being renowned throughout the 12th Corps for the way they did what was asked of them and more. They rallied to save the batteries in the very midst of the thickest fighting and bravely laid down their lives to hold the Union Right together. The artillery Captain Cothran singled the 107th NY out in his officer's report as being entitled to "great credit for both coolness and courage," and "the admirable manner in which it supported my battery during the fight." The 107th boys had earned the gratitude and admiration of not one but two batteries of artillerymen and officers.

10. Who Had Won the Fight

General Gordon reported that out of his brigade of 2210 men and officers engaged, there were 72 killed, 548 wounded, and 29 missing; in other words over one quarter of his men were lost from the ranks as casualties of one sort or another.

It was difficult to arrive at accurate death and injury lists for the two armies due to the chaotic nature of such a battle, however the official numbers reveal that the overall average number of casualties was about 1 in 4 men, some 23,000 total. September 17th, 1862 would go down in the record books as the worst single day of fighting on American soil with total losses of 3,600 men killed outright. Another 2,000 of the wounded would go on to die of their injuries. Many of the wounded were disabled in one way or another for the rest of their lives.

In spite of the horrific numbers, the battle was a tactical draw, with General McClellan claiming victory of the ground but in actuality having gained nothing but a field and a strip of battered woods. Two days later, on the 19th, both armies postured and threatened each other but only skirmished sporadically. General McClellan did not pursue the advantage he held in numbers, still stubbornly insisting that Lee had an enormous horde of fresh fighters at his disposal, probably concealed in the hills close by. This decision was considered by many, including President Lincoln, to be a terrible mistake, one that would ultimately cost Little Mac his job and the rest of the country two and a half more years of miserable warfare.

The next day, abandoning the invasion of the North, General Lee began to withdraw his decimated army back to safety across the Potomac. It is estimated that he had less than 30,000 troops left in fighting condition. Mac staged a weak pursuit that Lee easily repelled as he made the clean getaway into Virginia that he had so wisely planned.

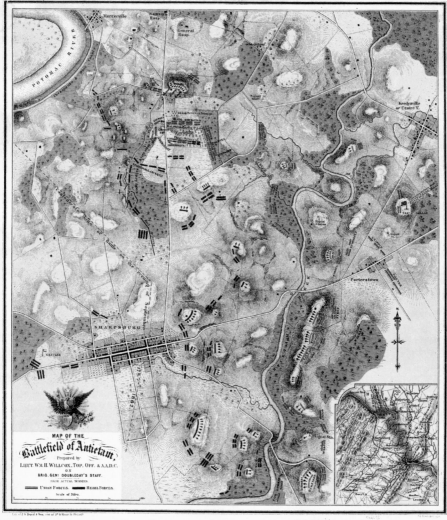

Map of the Battlefield of Antietam

General Joseph Hooker, who famously lost the Battle of Chancellorsville

Union Color Guard

A Sharpshooter on Picket Duty by Winslow Homer

Union Field Battery

Artillery Officers Relaxing

A Shattered Caisson

Dead Confederate Artillerymen with Dunker Church, Antietam

Father I canot write there are men dying all around me and they need My assiste. I should like to write you a long letter and will as soon as I can this has been a terrible Battle and I saw the worst of it our regiment was in the worst part of it and took the place of 3 regts that run. this is all the paper I have or can get & I have no stamps. I lost every thing I had in the battle part of the time I get some thing to eat and part the time I dont. good bye write as soon as you get this. direct to Washington.

send me some paper if you can if you send them to Washington we will get them

R. Harnden

Rufus's letter to his father after the Battle of Antietam

Gun Squad

Chapter 7   The Field Hospital

The next day I found time to write my father a longer letter describing how I remained at the hospital where there were now over one thousand men. I knew of eight or nine other hospitals around the field of battle, some holding more wounded than ours. I told him how the piece of shell hit me, grazing my cheek and cutting across my eye about like a deep pin scratch, then cut my eyebrow in two to the bone and up under the bone so as to make me feel very dizzy and weakened.

News of the battle and its aftermath came into the hospital by bits. Colonel Diven dropped by and told me the regiment had sixty-three casualties with twelve of them deaths that he knew of so far, thankfully not one of my friends being amongst that number. He said he was proud of us green boys as we had held up under the thickest part of the fighting and never gave in, while other regiments had lost their nerve and run. He also said that after I was wounded, our brave boys had saved the battery of cannons from capture and we would most likely receive a citation from that battery commander.

Word also came to me that our Division of eleven regiments might have lost one quarter of its men overall. Everyone said it was the worst day of fighting they had ever seen or ever even dared to think about. I reflected that we had been in the army for just a little over one month with very little training. I felt as tho I had been run over by team of oxen, body and soul.

For days after the battle, I tended to a group of boys who lay together under a tree outside the hospital. They needed water and food of which there didn't seem to be much on hand. With so few supplies, cleaning their wounds was near impossible. I was forced to tear up dirty clothing to use as bandages. My own blouse was caked with dried blood. Sometimes a doctor would come around and decide who must go to the operating tables. Other times one of those poor men would succumb to his wounds. I had two in my care who were shot in the belly; their agony being beyond description. The surgeons told me nothing could be done for them but to let them die as quick as possible. It was a terrible, sorry business. I heard that many times a doctor or friend would arrange a rifle in such a way that a soldier wounded suchly could shoot himself and hasten his grueling end. I scrounged as much morphine as I could manage from the surgeons and gave it to those poor fellows.

Several days later I heard that the 107th was encamped out on the battlefield, resting up, and would be employed to bury dead men and horses. We still couldn't tell who had won the thing and it didn't seem like any ground had changed hands.

I finally got a note from Tenbrook letting me know my friends definitely come through safe but they were sick of so many dead bodies lying about and smelling so bad. Edgerton had been overcome by the stench enough to make him swoon away and have to lay down up wind of the field.

After hearing about that, I walked out on the field and saw it for myself where hundreds of men were piled up in heaps, then buried in one grave. You could see arms & such sticking out of the ground, and the stench was awful or it was before it got cold at night. Dogs would dig them up and eat them. If the rebs or our men were too tall, they would take their foot and shove them in and crook up their legs. They would also haul five or six hundred men into a low place, then take a team of horses and a scraper and haul the dirt around the edges of them, and then men would shovel more dirt on until they were covered. That was true. There was no ceremony about the thing. Lord help me, I was getting used to the foul stench of war.

I went out several times over the battlefield and saw piles of horses¹ too. It took large numbers of horses and mules to move the cannons and ammunition wagons into battle. After unlimbering they were stood close by in case the battery had to move off again right quick. As such big targets, the poor creatures were killed off even faster than the men. Most of the horses they burnt up easily enough, since they were fat, having been well fed on fodder to keep up the great strength it took to pull cannons or tote officers about.

I wrote my family to say that they may have thought they had heard of the horrors of war, and so had I before, but when you go through what I did at Antietam, you would think you had never heard anything about it.

I hung onto my gun for three or four days after the battle until an officer of the regiment told me to put my gun and two or three others that lay about into the ground, bayonet sticking down, and make a tent with them to put over our company man, Johnny French.

He was lying down during the fight when a cannon ball struck him in the back and cut some of his ribs off and tore the flesh from his hip, making such a frightful gash in his back you could see his innards. There was no point putting him inside the hospital anywheres. We made up the tent and watched by him until he died. Then we carried him up to be buried and when we got back, our guns were gone.

So I had lost everything I had but my head and that was a very close call. Since then I had no blanket nor over coat nor tent. Nothing but a thin filthy blouse and no vest. I eventually found me a haversack and canteen left over from a man that died.

I saw six or seven other men out of our company in the hospitals. Three of the worst were very bad. One's arm was shot off and one had a minie ball go into his chin, through into his mouth, down inside of his neck, and come out of his shoulder. Believe it or not, he was getting along all right and might have come through.

I was recovering from my wound for many days. The doctor said I was concussed by the blast and needed rest but I was still able to assist at a fair number of operations once the surgeons realized I could be of help and keep a cool head around the blood and misery. I knew not how come this was true but it seemed to be so. It was as if my mind turned on and my emotions off so I could remain steady and not be pulled down by the gore.

Operations were going on constantly. All day long the surgeons performed amputations[2]. I witnessed twelve to fifteen of them up very close. The saw made an awful rasping sound as it cut through the bones of all those poor boys. The doctors earned the title of Sawbones for sure. Shattered limbs piled up next to the tables or got thrown out the windows of the farmhouse to be buried later.

I was there most of the time. I even held a man's leg while they worked to cut it off. The muscles didn't contract properly and so they sawed the bone off again. I took the piece to make a study of it. It was an inch long and got sawed off half way between the knee and the thigh.

After a week there were a few other less injured from our company at the hospital so we stuck together and helped each other out. We got tired of so many revolting scenes of pain and death around us and yet we were still alive and awful hungry so we laid plans to get something to eat[3]. We made up our minds, if there was any chickens about, we would have us some, but it turned out, we had something better.

We left the hospital area and come to a house occupied by an old woman and her son. We went to the barn and stayed all night lying in the hay loft.

Early the next morning we got up and saw a man was there. We asked him to let us have something to eat. He said they had nothing but we begged so hard, they finally took pity on us. They gave us a big rooster and cut it up ready to cook. They even let us have a kettle, salt, potatoes, and some green corn. We went out in the field and cooked it. We were so hungry we couldn't wait so we let the rooster get only half done and ate it. It was first rate.

Next we filled our haversacks with apples and went on to the next house. Well, two of us went up to the door and asked for something to eat. They gave us a big slab of bacon, enough to last us a week. Those folks were secesh but generous to us in person. The woman told us if we had come in the afternoon, we could've got some warm biscuits.

The idea of warm biscuits was too much for us to let go of, so we went back to our friend and conferred up a plan, then we lolled around under a tree till afternoon. The one of us that hadn't been to the house yet went over when we could smell the baking. He asked for something to eat for himself and the wounded man he was taking care of, which was me.

She gave him a whole pile of nice biscuits. She told him that there was a young fellow and an older man there that morning and they had begged off something to eat too. She said the young fellow had a bandage over one of his eyes and looked very sorrowful, adding that she pitied him. I didn't realize till then that I looked so poorly.

Two or three other times I got things to eat from this kind lady.

One day I was going by a house where lived a colored family. They invited me inside where a good fire roared in an old fashioned fire place, so I sat to get warm. The family had been eating breakfast.

I told them I would sure love something to eat but had nothing to pay for it.

The old lady of the house says to her daughter, "Come Lizzy, fly around and get this gemen something to eat."

Lizzy went to work and got me a good breakfast like I hadn't seen since Waverly. I had sweet potatoes, warm biscuit, bread, beef steak, gravy, butter, coffee, and sugar, cold ham and preserves. I guess they give me something of everything they had in their larder.

Well, the joke of it was, just as I sat down to eat, there was a knock at the door and both our doctors come in and caught me at it. Old Doc Flood always thought a good deal of me when I was sick.

He came up and took me by the hair and shook my head. Says he, "I've caught you at it, you rascal!" and he laughed to split himself.

I looked around and said "This is all right ain't it?"

"Yes," says he, "I'm glad to see you at it. It will do you good."

I fell in and ate every crumb and I believe it did do me good for I began to gain weight as soon as I got that wholesome food into my body. I had three or four meals at the same place and if ever I can repay them for all their kindness, I will do it.

After awhile back at the hospital, most of the men we were taking care of died and I felt well enough so I laid plans to get back to my friends. Our regiment now lay over at a place called Harpers Ferry about ten miles away from the hospital.

Me and another convalescent fellow caught a ride in a baggage wagon that was going over. Before we got very far, a man stopped us in the road and wanted us to help him find out who killed his hog. We knew it was probably some hungry soldiers encamped nearby but we didn't tell him so because what were we poor soldier boys supposed to do without anything to eat from the army most of the time. We were forced to steal from the citizenry just to survive. The man also mentioned that he had a sick Union Captain back at his house about a quarter of a mile away.

Now I had heard our Captain Wilkerson had fell out on the march to Harpers and was somewheres along the road taken down very sick. I hopped out of the wagon and walked with the citizen over to the house just in case it was our own good man. It was Captain Wilkerson all right and very ill with fever. I wanted to fetch Doc Flood to come see him immediately so I started for the regiment on foot and walked most of the night before I found some straw to rest on for a few hours till morning.

I started right off again early and wished I had a horse so I asked at a farm if I could lend one but they refused. Walking was so slow and tiresome that finally when I seen a horse out in a field, I found a bridle in a barn and took him. He looked youngish but I thought he might be about seven years old.

I got on him with a great deal of trouble. He carried on making mischief at a terrible rate but I managed to get him going in mostly one direction. A man along the road was awful surprised to see me ride that horse so. He said that it was a colt not even two years old and never been rode not even once. I thought so too by now for he would run with me a ways, fall down, then throw me off, and do anything else he could think of.

Somehow that horse and I made it to the regiment and just as I got the Doc to start back to the Captain, the owner of the colt runs up all in a fret. He had ran the whole way to cetch me when he missed his colt. He blowed a lot of hot air at me, as much as he dared, and then went home with his horse.

After that, I found our tent and the boys were awful glad to see me back. It was very good to all be together again. But I was so tired and run down I come down with the cursed dysentery the minute I got there.

1. Piles of Horses

At least one million horses would be killed during the course of the Civil War. After Antietam, General Williams wrote: "One beautiful milk-white animal had died in so graceful a position that I wished for its photograph. Its legs were doubled under and its arched neck gracefully turned to one side, as if looking back to the ball-hole in its side. Until you got to it, it was hard to believe the horse was dead." The burial teams left the horse and cleaned up the broken equipment and other dead around it. General Williams got his photograph.

2. Amputations

Amputation was a very common form of treatment during the Civil War. If a soldier was badly wounded in an extremity, the effected limb was simply sawed off, the stump sewn up, and prayers offered that the man did not get gangrene in the surgical wound and die.

The patient was first anesthetized with whiskey, opium, ether or chloroform and the ensuing operation took under half an hour to complete. The most commonly used pain killers were chloroform and ether, both of which had been put into use several years before the start of the war.

Chloroform was preferred because it was non-flammable and its fumes did not affect the doctors. The patient was rendered unconscious and then revived following surgery. Once the operation was complete, the wounded man was removed from the table and another brought right away.

The surgeons wiped their hands on their smocks and washed their implements in a bowl of bloody water before they started the next operation. Limbs were thrown upon a pile to the side of the table and buried later. Not surprisingly, a high percentage of amputees died from infection, over 1 in 4.

3. Foraging

The Union Army gave out two kinds of rations, a ration being what it took to feed a soldier for one day. Camp rations were of greater variety but only just filling enough. Marching rations for an army on the move had to supply enough energy to march for hours and/or fight. But both armies frequently ran out of food when supply lines came under attack, there was bad weather, or there simply was not enough available. Soldiers were then expected to hunt for food in the countryside. This was called foraging and often took the form of plundering citizen properties.

The Surgeon at Work

Embalming Surgeon and Dead Soldier

Field Hospital

Confederate Field Hospital at Antietam

Dead Horses

General Williams' White Horse Photograph

Foraging to Eat by Winslow Homer

Chapter 8   Harpers Ferry

The regiment's new camp was high on a mountainside made up of stone with a magnificent view. From our lofty perch we looked down on where the Potomac and the Shenandoah rivers flowed together into a mighty stream. We could see Harpers Ferry very plain tho it was entirely ruint by rebs by now, the railroad bridge being blowed to bits[1].

Harpers Ferry was famous among the boys for having been fought over so much, on account of the railroads and the arsenal there, and also for having been the site of John Brown's raid before the war, where he tried to start a slave revolt. Of course, he was captured and hung for it.

The ground was so hard up there on the mountain heights we couldn't bury the boys that were dying off from wounds. They tried to burn the bodies one day but the pile didn't take light because there wasn't enough fat on the corpses to cetch fire. But the worst problem we had was the water. There weren't none to be found, not a spring nor streamlet to be seen anywhere. Water had to be carried all the way up from the river and once again, it didn't agree with us. We got dirtier and sicker the longer we stayed up there and I think we stayed over a month.

Soon, our old windbag Colonel VanValkenburgh left the regiment to return to his life of ease and influence back in Washington. It seems he'd made a name for himself by what we boys done by saving the battery at Antietam. Now, I guess he'd seen enough of soldiering. So had we all but we could't leave, could we? Oh no. But he could. So he left us to starve up on that stony hill. We didn't think much of him after that.

Behind us in the countryside were orchards filled with fruit and wheat fields, so there was some fresh kinds of food for the boys to eat if we had strength enough to go out foraging for it, but most of the boys were too convalescent and rundown for such endeavors. I will give you a faint idea of what we then had to eat most days.

The army gave us[2] eight hard tacks, a small piece of salt pork, two spoons full of coffee, and two of sugar for a day. Hard tacks were a square shaped cracker made of flour and water, then dried out in an oven. If you were lucky, your hard tacks were not full of worms. Mostly they were alive with them. We called them dog biscuits or other names too vile for a godly man to mention. Those that could find a stamp wrote home begging some food and clothing be sent down to the regiment.

I couldn't send a letter to my own family until October 1st on account of having not a thing to write with. I have seen poor soldiers give a nice revolver for some postage stamps and paper. Myself, I finally begged a piece of paper off one kind fellow and a stamp off another.

Conditions were so poor in that place, it didn't surprise me when a horrible fever[3] came along and took us boys down. One after another we succumbed to its ravages, a number that soon included me.

First thing after the start of the dysentery I got a terrible headache. Tenbrook and I had to do guard duty anyway until I couldn't bear up a moment longer. For two days and nights, I laid sick out on the open ground. Finally Dr. Flood come by and put me into a hospital tent with Decature who was also taken very ill. Tenbrook was taken but not as bad as me. He went back to our tent where Wiggens and Edgerton remained. They were the only two of my friends who did not get sick at that time.

I became so ill with fever that Wiggins even took it upon himself to write my family and let them know of it in case I died. The doctor first thought the shell which burst close to my head

118

must have affected my brain, making it ache so, but then the fever come on me and so he knew it wasn't my wound that was causing it.

After a few more days in a tent, they moved me and Decature into a nearby barn for a hospital. The army kept their horses in one part of the barn and us in another. Actually, you'd be generous to call it a barn because it was really just an old rookery. The roof didn't amount to anything. I laid in an old mow on straw that had been lain on so much by the sick that it was all cut to pieces and stunk very bad. The men were so crowded in the hay loft they crawled over each other and climbed down ten feet to get to the floor, and that was crowded full too. We had two or three soldiers to nurse forty men, the most of us very sick.

One died the first day I was in that place and some others were nearly in the same fix. Wiggins saw to me and Decature, staying with us most of the time.

The doctor said we had what they call the Camp Fever and he would go across to Harpers which was down the hill only about half a mile and see if he could get a better hospital than the barn for us.

I had a fearsome headache most all the while. When I lay perfectly still my head would sometimes stop its aching if I was lucky. My fever came on about ten in the morning and held on through the afternoon and most of the night. My tongue was furred up and my stomach was bad.

One morning before my fever spiked I was able to rouse myself enough to write home on account of we had a some excitement I didn't want to miss, a visit from the President himself! He came to review the troops and speak with Little Mac. Will helped me out of the barn. Leaning on him, I was able to walk over to the officer's tents. There I seen Old Abe and his whole staff. They were fine looking fellows but I would like to SEE THEM DO THE FIGHTING!

I felt that if I ever got out of this business alive, I would never get into another trap such as I was in. The soldiers all felt so in our regiment. They said "get me back to Elmira and they may have their bounty and all they owe me!"

Rumors flew around that the reb General Lee and his staff were in Washington with a flag of truce, and another story was they had already sued for peace and would pay off the debt to the Union. I didn't see as any of that could be the truth because I didn't think we had beat them in the fight at Antietam. General Lee had taken his men off back across the Potomac into safety and Little Mac hadn't even gone after him.

I heard that Old Abe was very displeased with that result. He wanted Mac to give chase to the rebel army and try to cetch them but Mac just wouldn't budge. Mac said he thought it fully good enough that he and his army had kept the North from being invaded. In fact Mac puffed himself in the papers quite a hero on the subject.

Meantime, Dr. Flood was trying to get out a furlough for Decature and maybe one for all of us down with fever. He said if he got them they would be for two weeks and we could go home to convalesce. If we were too poorly to come back at all, we would get a certificate and a discharge as not fit for service. Our hopes were lifted.

But four days later we had neither our furloughs nor anything good to eat.

We soldiers had pretty hard times then and nothing to cheer us. They couldn't get any further hospital stores or provisions and we were in that bad place where the water didn't agree with us. We had laid around in the old encampments so much that we all got body lice. There was nothing to wash in, nor wipe on. For our victuals, we had soup and once in a while, coffee and rice, generally burnt. And of course, many of us was down with fever. I sure would have liked to see something good to eat.

Decature was worrying all the while about his furlough. It didn't help that Wiggins set him going about it. Then Dr. Flood finally came over and said he don't think he can get the furloughs after all. I tried to take the thing cool and got along with it the best way I could but I was plenty mad down deep.

Someone stole my pocket knife leaving me not just nothing in the world to eat but nothing to eat it with. I felt bad that I had lost every possession I owned or the army had give me but it could not be helped. I wrote home and asked them to understand my situation and please put up a small knife and a fork into a pencil box and send it by mail. I told them that and some food would come good too, though I knew my father would be upset to hear how I had lost everything in the battle or to thieving. I thought that Father would think I was finding fault at an awful rate but it was not so. What I wrote was the plain truth, but I dreaded to be a burden upon my family.

Dr. Flood let me only write a short letter for it tired me so to sit up. Many of the officers were taken down sick, including Colonel Diven. Our Major Smith said he would bet fifty dollars the war would be settled in six weeks. I sure hoped so.

News came that Old liar Colonel VanValkenburgh was elected to Congress once more. I heard too Captain Wilkerson was still suffering acutely from the fever. They couldn't move him and he remained at the farmer's house nine miles away. I thought he might never make it back to the company and that was a bad fix for us as the second lieutenant had turned out to be a perfect tyrant.

1. Harpers Ferry

Although the Virginian town was small and isolated, since it lay at the confluence of the big rivers in a natural gap in the Blue Ridge Mountains, its location gave it great importance during the war. It had two railroads coming through it over a bridge, and a firearms industry including an arsenal and an armory. The two sides fought over it constantly. It changed hands eight times during the war. By 1862, when Rufus got there, most of it lay in ruins.

2. Victuals

Rufus's menu was made up of simple fare, whether in camp or on the move. Food had to be non-perishable and shippable without any refrigeration so options were limited. Smoked beef or pork, salt, sugar, flour, some dried vegetables or legumes, coffee, and the infamous cracker called 'hardtack' were the staples of the diet. Occasionally fresh fruits and vegetables made it to the soldiers' tables but the army commissary rarely provided such perishable foods. Rather it was up to the troops to beg or steal fresh food of any kind from the local farms and backyards in the surrounding countryside.

Hardtack was a staple of the diet for the Union soldier, providing him with a source of grains that did not require cooking in the field. It was a small 3" by 3" biscuit made from flour, salt, lard, and water, then dried in a brick kiln called an oast. Manufactured in large, perforated sheets by northern factories, it was stacked and crated in blocks for storage and shipping. Sometimes the crates sat in a supply depot for months. By the time it was handed out to a soldier, it was not only hard as a rock, but usually infested with worms and weevils. The troops called them by a imaginative variety of disdainful names: worm castles, tooth dullers, sheet iron crackers, dog biscuits, and a host of other cruder names.

The men either gnawed them plain or cooked them. A popular meal in the field consisted of crumbled hardtacks, fried up with salted pork in a skillet and named 'skillygallee.' Soldiers also broke up hardtack using their rifle butts or rocks and stirred the crumbs into their morning mugs of coffee. The insects would float to the surface where they could conveniently be skimmed off.

A typical ration of hardtack was 6-8 crackers to last each man 3 days in the field. "Field rations" were what a soldier carried with him in his haversack when the army was on the move and there was no commissary service set up to provide for him. The haversacks quickly became encrusted with bits of decaying food. Except for hard tack, the food was given out uncooked and each man cooked it by himself or with friends over an open campfire in his own pan. Small groups of men often gathered to cook together. This activity became known as a 'mess,' perhaps due to the way they cooked everything mixed up together at once in a large communal serving. One's cooking companions became known as one's 'mess-mates.'

The Confederate soldiers ate somewhat differently than their Union counterparts. Their diet included bacon, corn meal, tea, sugar or molasses, oil or lard and again, scavenged fresh meats, vegetables, and fruits. For their primary source of grain, cornmeal, salt, oil, molasses, and baking soda were stirred together and cooked in a skillet of bacon grease over a campfire to produce 'johnnie cake'. The rebel armies had much less food available to them in general due to the South's inferior resources.

In fact, by August of 1862, Lee's army was close to starving and most of his men were living off scavenged green corn which wasn't doing any wonders for their stomachs. Lee invaded Maryland for a mixture of reasons. He thought he could liberate a neutral state from the influence of the Union and bring it into the Confederate fold. He wanted to threaten or possibly destroy the Federal supply lines around the capital city of Washington. And, just as importantly, he was desperate to feed his hungry army off the untouched fields of ripe summer crops in the farmlands of the as yet un-ravaged state.

3. Camp Fever

The doctors of the Civil War era did not understand the causes of typhoid. All they could do was provide a place for their patients to lie down and sweat it out or die. Typhoid was lumped in with measles, dysentery, and any other illnesses that caused high temperatures and was called 'camp fever.'

Like dysentery, it is a toxic bacteria that spreads from a diseased person's feces. Contaminated water, dirty hands, and flying insects spread the infected material quickly from man to man.

In the first phase of the illness, fever develops slowly during the day accompanied by headache, fatigue, coughing, and gastroenteritis. As the illness progresses, the fever gets very high, to around 104 degrees, leaving the patient unable to get up much of the time. In the crisis phase of the infection, which lasts about a week, a number of fatal complications can occur, with the fever remaining high all the time and the profusely sweating patient becoming delirious and dehydrated. The fever begins to subside after that leaving the patient extremely weak and debilitated. The whole process took about a month to run its course with a lengthy convalescence.

Harpers Ferry and its Rivers

Antietam Barn Hospital

Lincoln and McClellan meet at Antietam, MD

Union Officers Dining in Camp

Chapter 9   Fever

Following the writing of my letter home my blasted fever got so bad that I lay utterly prostrate alongside Decature for a week. The whole time Wiggens stuck to nursing us but then he took sick himself. Tenbrook took a turn for the worse too. They both ended up in the hospital after that.

Edgerton, the last of us left in our tent, had come down with only a slight case of fever. He wouldn't go to the hospital and wouldn't let Wiggens take him for anything before Wiggens got sick. The conditions were so bad in the barn that it scared him off.

He said that if a man went off to the hospital he wasn't likely to return, it being a much more dangerous place than a battle any time. He laid in our tent and got better by himself tho he said later he was awful lonely. The boys told me that out of the whole regiment of eight hundred men left since Antietam, at our lowest point, not even two hundred were well enough to do their duties.

At last, Dr. Flood was able to have us sick men moved out of the barn into an old stone house. The windows were all gone out of it but it was more comfortable. Decature and I stayed upstairs in one corner of a room together since we were among the sickest. I had a straw tick to lay on and a good blanket to cover me. In the other place I laid on the barn floor with a little rotten straw under me and nothing over me.

Slowly I began to feel better, not first rate but my head did not ache so much anymore and my fever was way down to about gone. I was very weak and took quinine. The doctors poked so much medicine down me I thought I might die from all their attentions instead of the fever.

Our new hospital place was called Boliver although it was no real place to speak of, only a few houses running back onto the hill up from Harpers. Diven's wife had come down to nurse him and he was getting better too. I thought she was a very good woman. When we were at Arlington Heights before, she used to come along and make soup for us or once in a while, a little porridge.

Out of the regiment there was 540 men still down with fever. Some of the doctors there called what we had Typhoid but Flood said he wasn't sure. I knew one thing, I was glad to have got through it as well as I had.

I walked out for fresh air one day and saw that the engineers had got a pontoon bridge[1] floated across the river above where the old railroad bridge was blowed apart. They had the trains able to run across again. I learnt I was going to get a coat, blankets, & such but the army was going to pay for them out of the wages they owed me. I thought it awful mean.

If you can believe it, by then all we got to eat some days was boiled cornstarch. The fever may have left me but I was down to skin and bones and the weakness had me held in a powerful grip.

Men began to desert[2] the regiment in droves and who could blame them. They had no tents, nor overcoats, nor blankets and the few healthy ones were scared to death of the fever. Plus Colonel VanValkenburgh had left us and most of our other officers were too sick to do much for us.

Another eight or ten men died in the stone house.

Decature's fever finally let go and Flood thought he would get along but then I myself thought it a great chance if he would live. He was very weak and emaciated, so much so that he could hardly speak. We bent down close to his mouth to hear what he had to say. Wiggens had looked after him until Wiggens himself had to lay down sick next to him. Then I heard that our Waverly friend, Henry Smith, died in the next house over. His mother had come all the way down there to nurse him. He was a good fellow. I was very grieved by the news and worried for Decature's future.

Soon after that, Dr. Flood came up one morning and looked over Decature and told me my friend couldn't live another hour.

I saw that Decature's fever and all his pain had left him and he was peaceful. He died around one o'clock in the afternoon on October 13th with Wiggins and I in attendance. We sat by him a long time after he breathed his last and we wouldn't let the other boys take him away. I tried to keep my feelings to a low boil as to how we poor boys had been served by the army. I know Wiggins felt the same. I could tell by just looking at him.

So two of our band of six from Waverly were taken by this infernal illness. We had all got through the terrible battle of Antietam where we was in the hottest part of the fight only to be now divided by an invisible enemy. I didn't care what name the doctors called that evil fever. I had seen all I wanted to of it and thought it fully as bad or worse than Typhoid. I prayed that the regiment wouldn't ever be taken down with it again.

After Decature died, I wrote home to my folks that they must go find his wife and break her the news that her husband had passed and the regiment would bury him in a coffin, speak for him, and mark his grave with a headboard.

I also told my father to NEVER, EVER think of going to war! I said, "Your patriotism may be aroused some times so that you feel like going but when you get there, and try it, you will find it is a political war and some of the worst games are played you ever heard of!"

I told him I wished the big politicians had to fight it out. That was what all the soldiers thought. The secesh boys felt the same way. I had spoken with a great many of the prisoners and wounded rebs and they all wished the leaders had to fight it out instead of us.

I pointed out to Father that our Colonel had left us on a cold bleak hill where the water was full of magnesia, poisons, & such and made us sick to our stomachs without tents, blankets, or even coats, or ANYTHING!

And HE went back to Washington with his good name to live in comfort with the other politicians while we was living a life of misery and many of us dying off, like our dear friends Decature and John Smith. Brave men who had fought hard for the Union cause.

I was not the only one saying it and feeling it. The Colonel had made his fine speeches to get us to come along, saying he would go through whatever we men went through and travel where ever we had to go and then he done this to us. I knew my father would think I was finding fault again at a terrible rate but I had to write it for I felt it that strongly. I was so mad my letter was written very poor with many blunders and blots which I hoped he'd excuse.

The day after Decature died, surprise! surprise! We got the knapsacks back we left behind before the battle. My dress coat, shirt, and blanket were taken out tho. I thought I should like soldiering better if there wasn't so much stealing and such gouge games played. If a man took off his shirt, someone would steal it.

Added to our troubles and sorrows, we heard the citizens at home had got together and sent some biscuits and apples to the hospital but the patients never seen any of them. And that was too bad because our worst problem after the fever was leaving us was getting hold of something to eat. Many of the boys were sending home for money. If they got it they could go down to town and get crackers and such things. I got a little milk with one of the two stamps a fellow gave me. Another fellow gave me a six pence and I got a piece of bread with that, so I had a little bread and milk which went first rate. I still had one stamp for my angry letter home so I sent it.

Mrs. Smith took her son's body home and we buried Decature that same day. I never felt so grieved as I did when I watched them lower him into the ground and shovel the dirt on.

I did have one streak of good luck while I was still in the hospital. They found an overcoat, some of the company did, and it had an R and an H on it. They said it was mine and sent it over to me. It wasn't mine but I thought I would hang onto it as the cold weather was coming on pretty fast. I sewed my name into it in large letters so they would know for sure it was mine after that.

At long last my father sent me some money and when I got out of the hospital, I got in some provisions that would build me and my friends up. I got crackers and cheese, some biscuit and bread, and some molasses to eat on it.

The regiment was left pretty small by then on account of all the men dying off or running away. In one day ten men left for parts unknown. They were leaving all the while and who could blame them for they had no tents nor blankets and some of them no overcoats nor anything else and they were used just like dogs.

My father wrote again to say he thought I sounded awful homesick and discouraged but I wrote back and told him not to worry because I would never desert. I seemed to handle the soldiers life better than most in fact, probably because I looked forward to letters from home, and wrote them. Surely we had nothing to make us feel good unless it was when we got letters or papers from home.

In spite of the bad fix I'd got in, I'd made up my mind to take things cool and feel as well as I could. I sold myself bad enough in going in for three years without lengthening it out in the least or taking it any harder.

Wiggins and the two Wills got better from the fever too. But Wiggins had worked himself into some bad kind of trouble with Decature's wife. It turned out that while Wiggins was nursing Decature in the barn, he used up his own little bit of money on food and a little milk for Decature. He wanted Mrs. Decature to pay him back for what he done for her husband, even though the poor man was deceased. They were drawing my family at home into this argument. Wiggins may have wanted my father to pay him for nursing me too. I couldn't see the point of it though Wiggins did take good care of Decature and me, that was for sure.

I didn't want to meddle in other folks business but I did say it wasn't Wiggins fault that Decature died. I heard that Mrs. Decature thought very hard of Wiggins. I hoped that she would see in the future that she was mistaken in regards to him. I never saw a man work so hard to make any one comfortable as Wiggins did Decature. He done more for him than I could of and was very kind to him right up till the moment he passed.

Another of our company from Waverly, John Armeth, also died. I felt terrible bad on account I remembered that I had once encouraged both him and Decature to enlist.

1. Pontoon Bridges

An army on foot could ford a stream if it wasn't too deep by simply wading through the water and driving its wagons across. But, if it was a more substantial waterway, a bridge had to be put up. The Army Corps of Engineers would step up to accomplish this all important task. If they had time and could span the water with a structure, like the Long Bridge or a trestle, they would build it, but if the water was too wide or deep, or if they were in a big hurry, they used pontoons to float a roadway across.

The pontoons and a huge number of tools and materials were carried by wagons in 'bridging trains' that accompanied the army where ever it went. A typical train would have 34 pontoon wagons in it. A pontoon was basically a large wooden canoe. Later in the war, the engineers made them out of canvas so that they would be lighter and easier to transport over land. Rows of pontoons were anchored 20 feet apart across the river. Then side rails and cross planks called 'chesses' were laid upon them to create the road surface.

2. Deserting

Desertion was a terrible problem for both sides in the war. As many as 1 in 5 Union soldiers, and 1 in 3 Southern men deserted at some point for some length of time. Numbers of men that deserted during the war reached well over 200,000.

The reasons for desertion were many. Someone like Wiggins simply wanted to go home to see his wife. He issued himself permission to take an extended leave and snuck away from the regiment without telling anyone where he was going. This was called "taking a French leave." Others left because they felt that their government had not upheld its end of the bargain made when they enlisted, namely to provide adequate food, shelter, supplies, a salary, and leadership. Some were scared, others were malingerers, that is men who just didn't want to do any marching and fighting, referred to as "skulkers." In the South especially, soldiers were apt to find themselves torn between duty to the government and their responsibilities at home. If wives and children were unsafe, ill, or hungry, men left the army to go home to care for their loved ones.

The official punishment for desertion was death but the two governments could ill afford to execute large numbers of their own troops. More common discouragements were flogging, branding, assignments of extra duty, fines, and other forms of physical discomfort and psychological humiliation. A notoriously dreaded punishment was called the "buck and gag" where the offending soldier was tied hand and foot around a piece of wooden rod with another stick used to gag him. He was then left for several long, helpless hours to be teased and shunned by his fellow soldiers.

The governments were often reduced to begging men to come back and would offer deals to entice a wandering soldier to return to his post. In March of 1863, so many men were absent from the Union army, that President Lincoln issued a blanket amnesty for 125,000 men in a sweeping gesture to lure them back into the military fold. But after the Battle of Gettysburg both armies began to execute deserters.

Pontoon Wagon

Pontoon Bridge

Burials

Chapter 10   Winter Quarters

At the end of the month of October, the doctors let me go back to active duty with the regiment. Amazingly, I never felt better in my life. I got so I thought I could eat an ox raw and felt pretty smart. I was getting fat fast even though mostly what we had to eat was hard tacks. I did not know what made me gain so, it surely was not high living. Food cost a lot and what little money I had from home didn't go far. Sweet potatoes was the cheapest thing I could find to eat.

Soon we were rumored to be going back to the fight. Our new marching orders came and we assembled to march with all our gear, but a man named Dr. Beadle from Elmira come out to the regiment and looked us over. Then he went to talk to Dr. Flood.

Once he had learnt the real condition of the men, where half were sick and most of the others in no condition to march yet, I heard he had went off in a huff to see General Gordon, still head man of our Division. When Beadle come back he gave us new orders to unsling knapsacks and go straightaway to our tents. Diven told us the good Dr. Beadle was going to write to the governor of New York and see about our not getting our pay and tell him how the men felt about that!

"Bully for Beadle!" the boys all said.

After that we were detailed to do picket duty for eight miles down along the Potomac, so we moved off the mountain closer to the river. I made ink out of pokeberries and penned a letter to my father asking for more money, food, and paper, tho I hated to have to do it. Also that Mary Wiggins should send John some five or six pounds of the baloney she puts up. We thought that would go a long way toward helping us build back our strength.

At any moment, we expected to be sent into winter quarters somewhere, maybe even back at Washington which is what we hoped for but the officers said not a thing about it. Some days we heard cannons firing in the distance. Either way we thought for sure we'd be swinging axes and building camps again before too long.

Then the army put Tenbrook up a rank to sergeant so he did not bunk with us for a long while. Not until they bumped him back down again because another man puffed himself shamelessly and sucked up to some higher officer so he could take Will's place away from him.

No orders came through to move so the three of us left, Wiggens, Will Edgerton, and myself built us a small log house. We had to carry the logs a good ways, they being poles the size that we could lift and tote. The tent was seven feet by six and the log walls were two feet high all around.

We rigged up our tent on top of the logs. We got no stove so we built a little fireplace in a corner. In the other corner we had a cupboard and on that side we slept, right on the ground. Wiggins on the backside, Edgerton next, and I in front. It was very comfortable quarters. I was so proud of the thing I made a little drawing of it to send to my father.

On account of desertion, we had six roll calls a day during that time. The last one at eight o'clock. Taps at one half after.

The water there in the new camp was as bad as up on the hill, it being yet another unhealthy place, and most of us got the dysentery again. I sent to my father for medicine to stop it double quick when one of us boys got the runs, for it killed men in that country. It could lead back to the fever and was four times as hard to stop as it was up North and therefore wanted something very effective to stop it. I also asked for a little medicine for colds.

As the fall deepened it rained a bunch and the roads became muddy. I thought the movements of our army would be retarded for that reason in the future.

Sometimes we saw signs of life among the rebs on the other side of the river. Their famous General Stonewall Jackson's army was rumored to be going to cause a stir around Harpers soon. It was said that Stonewall picked his fights and never lost them.

He never once backed down, hence his name. He may have been the best general they got but if he came our way, he would get whipped for sure. We told each other this sort of thing to bolster our spirits, even tho we knew it to before far-fetched.

The argument between Wiggins and Mrs. Decature dragged on with Wiggins writing to my mother about it and trying to get her to explain that he just needed back the money he spent on Decature because he wasn't in no condition to spare it being desperate for food, otherwise he wouldn't ask for it. I was on Wiggins side and told my mother so.

I finally got a gun again and it turned out I wouldn't have to pay for it as the loss of my other one was on the list of "lost in battle."

Some weeks after we'd built our log tent and was all snug and warm in it, we got orders to shove out in the pitch dark and bivouac farther down along the river. We wasn't well enough yet to do anything towards building ourselves a new shelter tent right away so we laid out doors for three or four days.

Soon we realized we would have to build winter huts all over again. There was an abandoned blast furnace and iron works off aways in the woods so we tried to haul bricks back to camp to build chimneys and fireplaces & such but still being in a convalescent state, we were all too weak. The nights dropped below freezing and the rate of desertion flew up again.

One day, we were called on parade and along comes General McClellan himself on his big black horse waving to us and making a big scene. It turned out Old Abe had removed him from head of our Potomac Army and put another general named Burnside in his place. We knew a little of Burnside from our Antietam fix and didn't care for him much. We were sorry to see Mac go because even if he didn't win large against the rebs, he took care not to risk too many of us neither. So we stood and waved back at the general, cheering for our little hero.

Not only were we cold out there along the river, but you couldn't hold all the lice there was in the regiment, what we called "body guards," in a bushel basket but it would overflow. As sure as you live, some fellows were alive with them. You could see them on their coats outside. There was not a man that didn't have them, officers and all. We'd got them from laying in the old campgrounds of those who'd come before us. I sent for my father to send me some camphor to fix them.

We were cold and itching up a storm but thankfully not so hungry one time for a little while. Dr. Flood organized a big rail car load of food be sent down from Elmira. This time we got it since it was sent in his care. There were boxes and barrels of potatoes, onions, & such things as to make a soldier sit up and take notice. The vegetables that came for us come good, I tell you. Thanks to the Elmira folks for their kindness to us, we got a peck apiece. The folks back home must have begun to see how we boys had been treated in the army.

We went on doing our picket duty along the river. I was on duty more than most because we still had so many unhealthy men. Some nights it snowed and those of us out on picket had to take the night on the ground. That was tough. God knows, there is no play about a soldier's life.

By Thanksgiving, my friends and I had all got boxes from our families. I got boots, a vest, gloves, and drawers from them and was very thankful, tho I regretted that I had by then some bad habits, like smoking and drinking. I felt bad I was not living more according to my good parents' wishes. The problem was that the life of a soldier, living rough, with danger and disease at every turn, and winter, to say nothing of not a thing to eat most of the time, is too hard NOT to drink, smoke, make mischief, and even be sorely tempted to start out for home.

We finally got another log hut built and mudded up with a fireplace in it. This time the logs was three feet high on a side with the canvas atop that so a man could stand up inside. We had an old rag in a dish of grease to light it at night and write our letters. We collected fence rails and barrel staves to lay across to make beds and get off the frozen ground. I had got so I could lay on a pile of five or six rails, three-cornered ones, and sleep comfortable. I used to think it was tough to sleep on a flat board but now I thought I would like to get a board to sleep on instead of a fence rail.

The first week of December come along and the army ran completely out of provisions. For two days we had not even a piece of hard tack to eat. You better believe there was some grumbling and growling amongst us.

One company even got its arms together and stacked them up like they was going to quit the service but their Captain told them not to do it and he promised not to make them drill. After four or five were arrested and thrown in the guard house, most of them went back to their tents.

They finally got us some hard tacks but they were so stale we had to break them up with a club or a rifle butt and soak them before we could eat the vile things. I also used to think it tough to have to eat just bread and potatoes with nothing on them as soldiers had, but now I found soldiers didn't get so many potatoes and so much bread. I would've liked to get them now without anything on them and if I did I would think I was living well. I dreamt of potatoes whereas before I'd thoughten nothing of them.

Many fellows were talking very strong of deserting. Among that number was our own Wiggins. He wanted me to go too but the thought of having someone chasing after me for always and ever was one reason I wouldn't do it. In case he went off, I gave him my piece of bone specimen to take to my father. The next night, sure enough, Wiggins was missing from our tent. Will and I supposed he had left. There weren't many but us cared that he was gone. He'd never done any duty to speak of and was a perfect pest to officers, doctors, and all.

Dr. Flood had told Wiggins he couldn't get a discharge or a furlough and since Wiggins had just got some money in a letter from home, I thought he started out for Waverly to see his wife and child.

I knew he would tell some awful stories about the war when he got up there, some things none of the rest of us ever heard of. I hoped they would believe not even half his stories, and even then they would be large.

According to his own story of the Battle of Antietam, he was in the fight a short time and fainted dead away from a shell blast, was carried off the field by an old soldier, and remained insensible for eighteen hours.

Yet he can tell five times more about that battle as the rest of us. He would tell things that any sensible man would know was impossible. He said eleven bomb shells struck within ten feet of his head. I saw most all the shells that come close to us, or rather saw where they struck, and did not see any strike so close to him as he tells about, nor did any of the company. Although our regiment was under a crossfire, and was said by some of the best officers to have been in a worse place than a regiment ever was without being all cut to pieces.

I was on good terms with Wiggins. We'd never had any fuss between us. I didn't blame him for going. I just missed him and felt homesick especially when I had to go by our army drugstore for some medicine. It made me lonesome for Doc Everett and even his store which I heard he moved to a new street. I wished I could see it.

When most of the boys realized Wiggins was gone, they said "Bully for him!" The Captain said he thought Wiggins had fell from grace when he deserted. He said he would cetch him if it was in his power.

I hoped Wiggins would get through safe and not get jailed.

There was a squad of rebel prisoners went by there one day and they sure looked tough. No overcoats and thin clothes. Our men found some of their pickets sitting up against trees froze stiff. There is no play about a soldier's life. It is a man's work. As I said, I didn't blame Wiggins for going, not in the least.

Building Winter Quarters

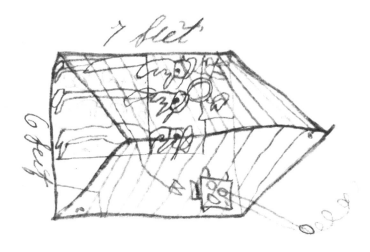

Rufus's Tent Drawing

Christmas Boxes by Winslow Homer

Christmas Eve, Harper's Weekly

Chapter 11 Virginia Mud

In December we were called up and did five days of hard marching toward the city of Fredericksburg on the Rappahannock River where General Lee was holed up for the winter with his reb army. I lost five pounds on that march, the conditions were so rough. The third day out the roads thawed and the awful mud delayed our progress.

While we was struggling to get there, we heard General Burnside crossed his boys over the Rappahannock, attacking Lee up hill against the city. Our boys called it the "Tall fighting." We got there too late for the battle. Our boys in blue were whipped something terrible. The loss of life was fearsome. Rumors were that our wounded boys laying on the hill pleaded with the boys coming up behind them to turn back on account of the useless carnage. We had no trust in Burnside after that, taking him for another bumbler and a fool.

After that march we went into camp near the Fairfax Courthouse in Virginia with the rest of the 12th Corps which had grown to an enormous size from new recruits and stragglers coming in all the while. Most of us in the 107th regiment had nearly broken down again from the forced winter march on account of still recovering our strength from the effects of the fever. I didn't think my health would ever be the same. I couldn't hold onto my weight and felt so trembly and weak that sometimes I just fell down and took a moment's rest where ever that might happen to be.

As usual, there was no way to tell what plans were being laid for us. Most days they marched us out somewheres and back. I figured we'd covered over one hundred miles in the first month we were camped there near the Courthouse. We lay out on the ground and got no pay. I heard there was 180,000 deserters from the army at that time. I thought if things kept on this way, there would be many more.

Seemed like every time our regiment got a nice camp all built up with ovens for baking bread and good log huts with fireplaces in them, we had to leave our cozy little establishment and throw away everything we had almost, then set off on another forced march to nowhere.

The so-called Fairfax Station where we now sat for Christmas was only a place where they unloaded provisions, tents & such. I called it Camp Misery.

By the railroad, it was only fifteen miles from the comforts of Washington. We laid out there in the woods without tents or anything to cover us and tried to sleep on the ground with our feet to the fire like to freeze some nights. One night one man did freeze. We awoke to find him stiff as a rail under his blanket. That's what I called really tough. It was such a lonesome place that the mules cried and whined all the while most dolefully. It made a man feel as though he'd give all his shoes and belongings to see civilization again. Some part of me wished I'd gone with Wiggens, the future be damned.

The army continued day after day to use us worse than dogs. One Sunday we received orders to build log huts and then in an hour or so later we received orders to pack up and move off again to we knew not where. We set off quick and marched to a creek where we spent the night on the ground. The next day we come back eight miles without stopping, pushed along very fast by the officers. It seemed the rebs had sneaked around to our rear and tore up the rail road below where we were.

In a nutshell this was how we soldiers were fixed at that time:
We were in shelter tents.
We had not been paid.

We expected to have good Sibley tents soon but didn't have them.
We had to lay on the frozen ground.
My hands were too cold to write letters home.
The Captain said he would cetch Wiggins if he could.
We had scarce rations and suffered from hunger.
We did not like it much.
Wilkerson was back with us. At least for this we were grateful.

Christmas and the New year came and went. We boys at last
got some more boxes of food and some garments from home
which come good, I can attest. On account of the snow and ice
everywhere, most of us thought there would be no movements by
the armies for the rest of the winter. We worked hard on our new
camp, tearing down a church about a mile distant. It was a good
brick building and provided us with supplies for our fire places.
We hated to tear that place apart as it was said to have been the
headquarters of General Washington in the Revolution at one time.

Finally we had first rate huts, all snug with even bunks to sleep
off the ground, but then on January 19th we got new orders to
march back toward Fredericksburg again. Seems old Burnside
just couldn't stand having to look out across the river at the
victorious General Lee's army hunkered down safe and toasty
warm in the city. Burnside was said to be hell bent on doing
something about it.

As we first set out on our long march the roads were frozen
solid through, rough with icy ruts but passable enough. After
a day, we got to a place they called Dumfries and camped. The
rest of the 12th Corps was strung out ahead of us with pontoon
wagons and all the rest of the heavy equipment for to cross at
several points higher up the river. They were preparing for a
surprise flank attack on Fredericksburg said Wilkerson.

The morning of the second day we awoke to a terrible mess.
During the night a cold, hard rain had come and started to thaw

the roads. It poured down in torrents all through the day. We set out but the roads were rendered quickly into rivers of mud. Alongside the roads the bushes and thickets were so dense no man nor horse could travel there. But to walk in the road was like walking on a sponge. A man had to step quick to keep from sinking out of sight.

I saw droves of mules go by where some of the poor creatures you couldn't see a hair on them for the mud, not even their ears. They had fell down and sunk so deep. Once in a while you would see a driver that had must of fell off his mule and dove head first into the mire for you couldn't see him neither except for his eyes staring out ahead at the road. After that, we couldn't move and had to sit tight. I never went through so much exposure in my life. My limbs ached and my hands shook so bad I could hardly feed myself or set up a tent. Thankfully Tenbrook was back by my side at that time to help me manage, having been demoted back to the ranks.

With the army stuck in place in the mud, General Burnside was forced to admit the defeat of his grand scheme. He called off whatever he thought he was up to on the third day. Some of the boys told me they'd seen a reb sign across the river, with words printed in large letters which said, "Great Union Victory! Old Burnside Stuck in the MUD!" I reckoned Burnside's humiliation must have been complete.

So next, they engaged us infantry building corduroy roads[1]. This being where you laid large logs down the sides of a road, then laid smaller logs across them side to side over the mud so there was a hard but bumpy like to shake your teeth out surface to travel on. That was the only way they could get provisions in to the army because of the terrible fix we were in.

We heard the boys had taken to calling the movement Burnside's Mud March[2] and that Old Abe was so upset with it that he fired Burnside and brought in a new head man, named Hooker, the same general from the 1st Corps we had gone to help out at Antietam. He'd been shot in the foot on that battlefield but was now fully recovered. The boys said he was a hard fighting man but rumored to be rather fond of his liquor and female company.

1. Corduroy Roads

When traveling got this bad because of mud, teams of infantry were commonly drafted from the regiments to construct roads called 'corduroy' roads. They were pretty much what they sounded like, ribbed roads made of horizontally placed logs. These were created by entrenching two large beams, called stringers on either side of a dirt road, about 8 feet apart and running parallel to each other like railroad tracks. Then smaller diameter logs were placed crosswise upon the stringers right up against each other where they were secured with spikes. A layer of sand or dirt was added to smooth the bumpy surface to some degree so that men, horses, and wagons could pass along with fewer teeth rattling jolts. Surprisingly, a well built corduroy road could last for up to 10 years, even in a wet climate.

2. The Mud March

By the beginning of January, General Burnside had grown desperate to redeem his good name and the fortunes of his army. He began to hatch what he thought was a brilliant plan. He intended to use a page from Robert E. Lee's handbook and employ the tactics of deception and surprise.

Counting on the fact that no one in his right mind would try an offensive across an unfrozen river in the dead of winter, he determined to make one and take the rebel army off its guard from a flanking position. To flank an opponent means to attack from the side where defenses are weak.

First he would stage a mock renewed assault at Fredericksburg where he had crossed the Rappahannock before but in fact he would march the bulk of his army very quickly and secretly some ten miles north, cross the river on pontoon bridges that his engineers would put in place before the arrival of the army, and roll up Lee's left flank in an elegant coup de grace. The pontoon bridges and the element of surprise were key parts of Burnside's plan.

Lincoln did not like anything about the risky plan and tried to warn Burnside that it was unrealistic to try such a thing in winter, but Burnside forged ahead with his idea. He observed that the month had been cold and the roads were frozen solid. It seemed to Burnside that they could be travelled on.

According to General Williams, his division left Fairfax Station on the 19th of January to join the rest of the 12th Corps on the journey up river. It was very cold, the roads were rough but frozen solid. The first day they were able to travel a good distance and camp without many problems at a place called Dumfries.

January 20th, General Burnside began his grand move. The engineers were sent out on the road to the north with the five bridging trains; the vast army hard on their heels. During the early morning, the skies darkened and the wind blew hard. Soon, a torrential, ice cold downpour began that lasted for several days without letup.

Within hours, the rain began to thaw the frozen roads and turn the melting earth into a soup of sticky mud. Treacherous holes developed that were so deep that mules disappeared into them and drowned, detectable only by the few bubbles that drifted to the surface of the muck. The heavy pontoon wagons sank to their axles and teams of horses literally dropped dead from fatigue. Their drivers threw ropes over the wagons and tried to draw them by hand through the ever-worsening quagmire.

General Williams wrote to his daughter about the Virginia mud and how it enveloped them that day:

"In the morning we had a precious sight. The frost had all gone and mud of the stickiest and nastiest kind had taken its place. The rain was still pouring, but we began our march at 7 o'clock, and such a march! On either side of the road was the densest forest of scrub pines, a perfect thicket. There were no side roads, no turning out, no getting into fields, but right onward through the saturated clay man and beast were compelled to travel, every wagon deepening the profound depth and every drop of rain softening the lower depth profound."

Burnside could not face the prospect of giving up. In the evening after twelve hours of terrible struggle, he ordered two days rations and whiskey for all the men and ordered them to keep trying the next morning. It was said that he himself drew on the wagon ropes for a time over the course of the next day. But it was simply not within their power to drag the heavy wagons through the deepening mud. The pontoon bridges could not be put up, morale plummeted, and to make matters worse, the element of surprise was totally lost. Rebel pickets on the other side of the river had long since figured out what Burnside was trying to accomplish. They taunted the exhausted federal soldiers, laughing and shouting out things like, "Burnside stuck in the mud!" "This way to Richmond!' and "Yanks, if you can't place your pontoons, we will send help!" General Lee even ordered his men to plow areas of the bank on his side of the river so that if Federal troops somehow managed to come across they would find themselves clawing through mud once again. Will Edgerton wrote to his mother on January 24th about the 107th's trials:

"We have had the hardest march that I ever saw. It rained 3 nites and 2 days in succession which made the mud from shoe deep to nee deep. I have waded creeks that was from nee deep up to my waist. It was so cold that the ice, 2 or 3 in. thick, floated down the swift watter. It freezes nites and thaws through the day. We are on the march where for I don't know in great hosts."

On the 3rd day, Burnside finally accepted defeat and ordered his sadly overexposed troops back into their camps but the unfortunate Army of the Potomac was stuck so fast in the Virginian mud that it was unable to receive supplies and feed itself even after it settled back into its encampments.

The Mud March

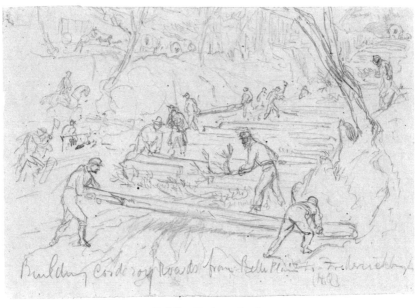

Building Corduroy Roads

Winter Quarters

Inside A Winter Cabin by Winslow Homer

Chapter 12   Hope Landing

Eventually, on January 31st of the new year, we were moved into another camp along the river at a place called Acquia Landing. More men simply lit out for home, feeling overly discouraged and too broken down to go on. We had no news of Wiggins.

Once again, it seemed that our hopes for the war to end any time soon were to be dashed. I wished fervently I'd listened to my mother and father and not gone to the regiment. But I done it and there was no use grumbling. The only reason I would desert would've been to see my parents and friends but I would've been ashamed to show my face wherever I was acquainted. So you see, it wouldn't work. I looked upon soldiering as my duty and couldn't get away honorably so I made up my mind to stay until discharged by proper authorities.

Though I did long to see my folks back in Waverly, when I had the chance at a furlough, I gave it away to the men in the camp with wives and children at home. I knew their families were in suffering conditions and needed their men home. Such men wanted the furloughs more than us younger men. I hoped I would have the privilege of seeing home again but I knew if I died where I was, it was for a noble cause. Well at any rate, I clung to that thought lest I drown in doubt and homesickness.

We did hear the very good news in January that the President had issued a pardon for all deserters. If they would just come back to their regiments they could have a clean slate. I wondered if Wiggins would take up Old Abe's offer. The chaplain said he might go back to Waverly on a furlough and fetch him if he could.

They called the place we now stayed "Hope Landing," a bad joke for us boys. There was no hope about the place, the conditions were so terrible.

We were like a ship on the tumbling waves of the ocean. We knew not when we would receive orders to march, and when we marched, we knew not where we were going nor how far, nor for what purpose. We went wherever we were called upon to go. Even if it was through mud up to our knees and that we did many a time since we came into Virginia. It was a terrible place for mud.

The whole month of February, when I turned eighteen, the roads were mostly impassable. Nothing could move but cavalry and they had an awful time of it. There were two or three mounted regiments passed by us one day, going back from the front to Stafford's Court House. They had some rough times getting through. The roads were like creeks, the mud coming up to the knees of the riders. A great many of them were thrown from their horses, head long into the soup and became completely buried. I tell you, it looked rough to see the poor fellows struggling in the mud with their feet in the stirrups and their horses floundering in the dirt.

During that time, I received a letter from home that spoke of my brother Edwin going up to our relatives in Port Byron to work in our uncle Dr. Button's apothecary. The news upset me greatly because Port Byron was a nest of Coppers and I did not like to think of him amongst those folks. I guessed my parents sorely needed the money or they should not have sent him up there. In Port Byron folks said, "Let them keep their slaves and even have slaves in the territories if they want, just as long as we make peace with each other and stop all this killing."

Whereas in Waverly we believed that slavery was a terrible sin and must not be allowed to take hold in the territories. We even had families in town who helped negroes fleeing the South to get up North and settle or move along to Canada. Tho these things were mostly done in secret, I'd witnessed these activities myself.

My father believed in hard work, equality, and service to others in God's name. A man ought to do his own work, or pay someone else a goodly wage to do it, not make another do it for him for free. Therefore, no slaves. This was how he explained the matter to me. Father had some powerful harsh opinions on the subject of my mother's relatives up there in Port Byron. It was like the division in the country was echoed inside our own family which made for a painful situation, especially for my mother.

If Edwin was slated to go work up there, my family must have been in very tight circumstances but I could do almost nothing at that time to help out. We saw no pay from the army at all. Edgerton and I worried most continually about not being able to send money to our folks at home. Edgerton's mother was always in a very bad fix, having been so sorely ill used by her scamp of a husband. Will continued to fret about her most all the while.

Edgerton, Tenbrook, and I at least had a tent fixed up again with a few other fellows. But one of us was usually feeling poorly enough to be staying over in the hospital. Our rations didn't last out the week they were supposed to. We fried our pork and then our hard tacks in the grease, and then we made our coffee in our drinking cups. I got so tired of the same thing day after day. A dog wouldn't eat it at home. but as I've said so many times, the army treated us worse than dogs.

If we ever got payed a few dollars we had no choice but to spend the money on food to keep body and soul together. They gave us but one candle a week for our tent.

So many men were missing from camp they tried to clamp down by doing roll call three more times a day and punishing men they caught out. They could've shot them for desertion but then there would've been even fewer of us boys left to fight.

We still heard not one thing about Wiggins but when I wrote home, I requested they hand the letter off to him if he was there, if not to him, then his wife. I wouldn't do anything toward his being caught.

At long last, spring started to come along in the month of March but it found me in a convalescent state once more. I'd got a very sore leg. My ankle was swelled up pretty bad. I guessed it was a kind of a pox. The leg broke out in bad sores though I hoped it would get all right soon. I'd been on sick call lately, but I finally told the lieutenant I should not go to sick call anymore. I had taken medicine enough. Dr. Flood told me not to take so much but the other doctor would keep poking it down me.

It was then, because I felt so poorly, I first started to think that maybe I could get out of the regiment by becoming a hospital worker on account of my past experience with Doc Everett. That would suit my constitution better than all the exposure and marches & such because I felt that I couldn't stand it since the fever. It seemed like every time we had a hard march and had to carry so much load, it broke my health down all over again.

To make matters even worse, the whole regiment began to be visited by another wave of deadly disease. Flood called it congestive brain fever this time. Many of the boys went down with it. They kept us awake at night with their hollering and carrying on. Most of them that got it died including a few from our company.

When my leg finally got better, I hauled myself back to active duty. We kept building roads but even bigger ones, wide enough for battery wagons. And out on the bay, we watched the engineers putting up pontoon bridges to take us we knew not where when the roads finally dried out.

I met a wealthy man one day who lived over near Fredericksburg. He offered to bet all he was worth that the war would be finished in three months because there was a large spring that broke out on his property three months before the Mexican War and dried up three months before the close. Well, it broke out three months before this war commenced and it dried up a week ago. Some of the boys thought it a wonderful thing, but I couldn't see it in that light.

Colonel Diven also thought the war would close soon, saying the summer would surely finish the thing. But then he too left us and took to spending so much time back at Washington attending to his other business or politics that we got a new officer in his place. His name was Colby and I thought him a much better man for the job than Diven ever was.

On March 20th, General Hooker himself came out to review our Division and in spite of all our sickness and desertion, he pronounced us in excellent form.

Then Diven visited at the end of March and made a speech to the regiment to raise our moral which I thought was pure hogwash the most of it. Next thing you know, he hightailed it back to Washington again only to return a little later to try to show us off in front of Old Abe when he came out to review the troops.

As we were passing by the President, Diven wanted us to perform a fancy quickstep but to our utter disgust he made a total hash of calling out the orders and we got all bungled up. We heard later that General Williams told Diven off, saying that he had single handed ruint the occasion for the whole Division. After that we were done with Diven for awhile. As I said, so many games were played. Most of the officers were always puffing themselves up, except for General Williams and a few others like Wilkerson who were made of sterner stuff.

Then we learnt from our officers that Diven, the old laurel seeker, had his choice to stay with us for the coming summer and have us do provost duty right there where we were at Camp Hope. We were all, officers, doctors and men in favor of staying put and not going into the field because of our illnesses. First Diven said that he would leave it up to us to decide but when we made the decision to stay where we were, he changed and said he would resign if we didn't go out to fight. Of course, we all wanted him to resign. Then he changed his tune again and said it wasn't up to us and he wanted us to go into the field and that was it, we had to go with him or be charged with desertion. After that all the boys were down on him, only more so.

If ever there was a fated regiment, we were it because men kept dying off from one thing or another. We were called so by the Medical Directors and every one.

For instance, we were all perfectly astonished when William Cooper, the cousin to one of my new tent mates and a teamster of the toughest sort, was telling me one day how perfectly healthy he was and had been all along. A few days later, he was taken to the hospital, turned spotted, became out of his head, and by night he was dead, and even buried before dark.

We also had one case of the real small pox. A man went on furlough and brought it back to camp with him. Some of our men slept close to him and probably had it too. We were in an awful pickle those days.

It turned out the Medical Directors heard that Diven had ordered us into the field and so they came down to examine us again. They took one look at us and was so mad that they arrested Diven and even poor Dr. Flood for having said we was fit for service when we had contagious diseases like the smallpox and brain fever going around.

Diven was not really a bad sort but he had nothing of a military man about him. Every time we went on inspection or drill he made a fool of the thing. Any one of one hundred privates in the regiment would have made a better Colonel than he was. And I considered by then that VanValkenburgh was nothing but a MURDERER! He had three or four offers to keep us green recruits in Washington way back in the beginning but he wanted laurels too and after he got them, he left us. This after marching us in hot weather before we got acclimated, until we got so weak, the roots of the fever started and I guessed we'd never get rid of it.

Very few of our officers died of sickness, tho we had lost a few. They didn't have to tote any of what we did, they mostly had horses to ride, and they didn't go through the exposure the boys had to take. That accounted for it.

We did have one rich note[1] that spring. One that cheered us all up considerably.

A corporal over in the 13th New Jersey, one of the boys in our brigade that had been with us all the while, and was a very nice fellow, everybody supposed he was. Well, he was taken sick the other day, and laid down in his tent and delivered a pair of twins! That was a first for us I can tell you. I thought him a profitable and productive corporal, doing all he could for his country!

It turned out he, or rather she, was wife to one of her tent mates and had come along with him into the war out of love and kept the secret all this time, marching and fighting by her husband's side as good as any man could have done. Of course the army sent the little hero and her twins on home but her husband was stuck fast, just like the rest of us poor sad sacks.

We had to work pretty hard those days for a spell, in spite of our travails. The army was getting up forage enough on hand so that when the Corps moved out to go fight, they would have it all ready to send to the supply trains and load it. It was heavy work. The sacks were sewed up and held four or five bushels each. They weighed 280 to 300 pounds and were filled with oats and corn mixed. The bales of hay we had to load were not quite so heavy.

Then our friend Wiggins showed up one day in April, back under the President's blanket pardon for deserters. Turned out, the Chaplain had gone up to Waverly and persuaded him. We were awful glad to see him and to know he wouldn't be hunted down and shot or thrown into prison.

Since Tenbrook was reduced in rank and had come to tent with us, the four of us friends got a good camp rigged up again. We hooked two tents together and covered over a log tent that a captain in the 13th NJ had lived in. There was plenty of good wood close by for our fires and water was down the hill just a piece from us. The four of us slept in one big bed and kept nice and warm. We had good times together again.

The roads at long last began drying out. The army paid off some of the regiments. By these two events we knew they were getting us ready to move, very soon, for the spring offensive. One day the artillery and cavalry started out. We heard heavy firing close by that day and the day after. We still didn't know if we would join the brigade and go to fight with them or not. They gave us some rations of whiskey at night after we were through with the days working to load the forage. I figured if I got paid, I'd send it home for my father to use. Wherever I was headed, I wouldn't be needing it as much as they did back in Waverly.

1. One Rich Note

Women disguised themselves and served in the Civil War for all sorts of reasons in addition to wanting to be with their men, like the desire for a life of adventure, to fight for the cause, to run away from things like arranged marriages, or just for the money. Not all of them were caught. Their ruse was detected only if they fell ill or were wounded in the torso so that a doctor discovered the truth of their sex while examining them. They were not punished as a rule and some eventually collected their soldiers' pensions openly. Reportedly most of them served with bravery and determination.

One of the most famous examples was Loretta Velazquez from New Orleans who not only raised but equipped her own regiment after the death of her husband early in the war.

She went out looking for a little excitement dressed as a Confederate officer. Under the adopted name of Harry Buford, she served exceedingly well, was wounded twice and received citations for bravery before she was discovered. Undaunted she became a secret agent for the South and eventually wrote a book about her harrowing adventures.

Francis L Clalin, also known as Jack Williams

Chancellorsville House

Soldiers Waiting before Chancellorsville

Chapter 13   The Road to Chancellorsville

We got marching orders on April 25th to set off at six AM in two days.

The day after the order come the weather started off a beautiful spring day. I remember that day clear as a bell. I cut hair for the boys all morning. I started on Tenbrook. I shingled his hair off close, first hair I ever cut in my life. Then the boys were all after me to cut their hair. They said I cut equal to the best barbers.

Later, when I came off guard duty in the afternoon, I got a life boat. Will and I went across the bay after fish. After we got started the wind come up and began to blow a perfect hurricane. Well, we wouldn't back out so we had a rough old ride. The waves would dash over us and we got plenty wet, laughing and enjoying ourselves. When it began to rain hard and get rough, we rowed back across. We could barely get in to the dock for the fierce rocking of the boat. Our muscles were so cold, stiff, and sore we couldn't hardly walk on dry land but we were luckily not too lame the next morning when we got ready to march.

The morning of the 27th, there were only 250 of us in the regiment well enough to fall in to get our marching rations. The usual: hard tacks, coffee, sugar, and salt pork. They gave us five days rations in our knapsacks and three days in our haversacks besides. Though we heard the paymaster had come to pay off the regiments what Uncle Sam owed us, we never saw him as usual so we did not get any pay in the end.

When we got going along the roads, organ grinder style as they say, marching in time to the drums, we heard there was fifty thousand men in our grand Division, under the command of a General named Slocum. We did not, also as was now usual, know where we were bound. Rumors flew up and down the ranks but to no purpose.

They boarded us on a steamer and we rode her further up the bay to a place called Kanes Landing. We got off and marched some more. Wiggins, Tenbrook, and Edgerton were there with me, excitement building, our fears forgotten. We thousands of infantry made the heavens ring when we sang "John Brown's Body" keeping time to the music of our bands. Singing greatly aided the boys in keeping up our patriotic spirits and enthusiasm for the project at hand. A great deal of it was done.

One old fellow we passed along the road, took off his old beaver hat and remarked to us, "Wall! You uns be right smart singers you uns be. I never heerd such a mitey big sing in mi life afore!"

Immediately after saying this, he planked a size twelve boot and his old hat in the road, crushing it down into the mud and leaving his foot 'thar' until we passed by. I guessed it was a country expression of his admiration.

One night during the march, us friends got detailed off and when we got back most of our rations were gone, stolen. Now we had one day's rations to last eight, so we knew we would have hard times with no food to speak of. I didn't think I could stand the marching. We seemed to get no rest at all.

We finally we got to a large river and had to stop to wait for the engineers to come and put up the pontoon bridges. I sat down and wrote to my father. I told him I'd decided to go through it, whatever was coming, and not flinch. I thoughten I had stood the march better that I imagined I would, though my feet were blistered very bad and my boots and socks full of blood.

Then, Surprise Surprise! They actually came around and gave out some of our allotment. When they paid us, Wiggins didn't get a thing on account of his taking a "french leave" like he done when he deserted. He was very put out over it. I gave him some of mine and another fellow a dollar for an old pair of shoes. They were not as good quality as mine, but larger.

The place we were stopped at was called Kelly's Ford. Once again we weren't allowed to have a fire or loud talk, since it was reported that the enemy were on the other side of the river in large force. I had begun to think that half the strategy for winning a fight was in hoodwinking the enemy to believe you had either more or less troops than him so he laid the wrong sort of plans for engagement.

In the afternoon Old Joe Hooker and his posse passed by us. There was such yelling you never heard. It was a regular 'bayonet charge yell" from the whole division. In our great enthusiasm for our new General we forgot we was supposed to be quiet. There was high hopes he would do a better job of it against Robert E. Lee than Burnside or Mac ever done.

Word came along that the pontoon bridges were twelve hours behind us and that would make a delay. We had to sit and wait. A soldier spends a good deal of time in the field 'hurry up and waiting.'

Diven was back with us but I hated to think of going into a fight under him, the old battle hater. He was so excitable. We did have a cool man in Colonel Colby. I feared he might be coming down with one of the fevers as he was feeling poorly on the march. It turned out I was right for he wasn't able to go into the coming battle with us.

We expected to move out that night with the 11th Corps crossing on the pontoons before us. We were surprised when they sent our 12th Corps first, but there wasn't much interference from the rebs. They must have withdrew when they seen so many of us crossing for I think the engineers had put up three bridges to carry us all.

That first river was called the Rappahannock. After we crossed it, we were upon rebel territory. They annoyed us greatly, burning the bridges over the smaller rivers and harassing us with sharp shooters and guerrillas fighters until we reached the the second large river called the Rapidan.

My heart was beating pretty good by then, after the sharp fight at Antietam I knew what we were getting into. There were two hundred cavalry or so out on the road ahead of us. I began to hear exchanges of gunfire as the horsemen encountered the first cavalry pickets of the johnnies' army.

General Williams was in the lead when we come up to the bluffs along the river. I watched as he sent out two lines of skirmishers on either side of the road to protect us while we men in the first companies climbed the banks and overlooked the water. A wooden bridge there was burnt to the water line by the rebs, just the charred pier timbers jutting up were all was left of it. The water was cold and moving very fast. Rebs had a large party watching us from across the river entrenched in the woods and in a house on the opposite bank. They waited to attack us if we started to rebuild the bridge.

General Williams and his party of scouts studied the water and talked things over. Unfortunately, there was no artillery with us to use on the rebs opposite. The scouts went out and established that there were some shallower places where infantry might cross on foot. So Williams gave out his orders to our officers that we were to cross as best we could in the shallow places and attack the rebs on the other side.

We didn't know that the General also sent two regiments, one upstream and one down, to cross at other places out of sight and come around behind the rebs and grab them up in a pinch.

When we got the order, we practically threw ourselves into that cold water, screaming and yelling our heads off. We held our rifles up high and waded deeper and deeper to where we had to hold hands to keep from being swept away and drowned. The water came up to our arm pits. Even up to our necks in places but we kept going. We slung our cartridge boxes on our bayonets to keep them dry. The rebs took aim at us and began to fire and picked off some of our boys, but the next minute they were surrounded and taken prisoner. Their attention had been held by the surprise of us fording the river and they'd forgot to watch out behind them.

Then our company was assigned to guard some of them reb boys. We had over 125 of them captive, I believe.

As was becoming my habit, I struck up conversation with a couple of them. They said, "We reckoned as how you yanks warn't no slouches and stood water mighty waal end they afeered that thar boys might get a goldarn licken when we uns cetched up on to 'em."

"Say Johnny," says I, " how far ahead are your forces?"

"Waal yank," he says, "its a mighty smart ways, a screech and a go by a level and a right smart turn, and you uns be thar. Say yank, hev yer any tanglefoot or terbacker? I reckon as you uns hev a right smart of both."

I had to tell him I had some of neither and he was awful disappointed to find us yanks had none of such fine luxuries.

After that the engineers came in an put up a temporary bridge on top of the old piers. This was accomplished within several hours but it still took until midnight to get the whole 12th Corps, wagons and all, to cross. A hard rain had begun to fall. We'd never dried out from our river dip so we continued wet through and through, cold to our bones. Even my shoes were filled with water and sloshing. I guess the officers decided since we were already damp from our little splash we might as well keep marching. We marched that dark night until at last they let us lie down to rest. We had no tents and by morning our wet clothes and sodden blankets had stiffened up in the cold air. I felt like we had been drowned just like rats and died after all.

Chapter 14   Fairview Farm

Regardless of our state of chills and exhaustion, we were called up at daybreak and after a hasty bite, we resumed our endless marching. Our route took us along an old plank highway so worn down in places the boards were buried under almost a foot of mud and dirt. We struggled down that sorry excuse for a road all day long. Our progress was once again impeded by guerrillas.

There was no sign of larger enemy forces until we came to a crossroads where there sat a little house back off the road aways. It looked like someone's old deserted meeting house or some such thing for there was no sign of habitation. As we marched through the clearing beside the house, enemy artillery suddenly opened fire with shells from the right side. We held up to take cover. Since General Williams had our Division in the lead, he sent two more regiments to go and clean out the enemy battery before we went forward.

There was a short but intense engagement while our men accomplished this task. The rebels ran off and we went on again as before without interruption.

During that day, the boys were somewhat given to foraging along the way, although it was strictly forbidden. Quite a lot of stock was taken off the farms around there. Cattle, sheep, and hogs. Some were shot, some carried off alive and stowed away in the wagons.

At noon, when we had stopped and were cooking up our fresh meat and drying out our clothes, an attempt was made by the officers to find out who the guilty parties were.

One fellow who was found to have mutton, got let off by proving he had not fired his gun. Instead he had carried the sheep all the way to camp on his back, butchering it while the boys were bringing in fencing for fires. The rest of us covered up any way we could, telling the officers it was rabbit or other such nonsense.

We were so ravenous for the meat we could not hold back and the spirit of mischief came over us. Many incidents of this character occurred during the day. But soon enough we heard the deep booming of cannon fire further down the river and the spirit of revelry and mischief was replaced with apprehension and anxiety. Wilkerson told me what we were hearing was coming all the way from Fredericksburg where our forces had begun to shell that city heavily, thereby signaling the opening of battle.

We were enjoined by our officers to keep very quiet and were marched rapidly again in the direction of the firing. Everything seemed to portend a great confrontation close at hand.

We marched along the same plank road until we come to another much larger clearing. Night was drawing near so we made camp there, a short distance from a large brick place they called the Chancellorsville House¹. It was all gaily lit up for it was now the house where General Hooker and his staff stayed, namely it was the headquarters for the great Army of the Potomac.

Our clearing was across the road from headquarters off on a hill. There was a small farm there from which the family had fled. Behind the house lay a tiny cemetery. A sign to the side of the door called the place the Fairview Farm. It overlooked the surrounding fields and woods, a perfect spot for artillery. General Williams parked us there and took the house for the 12th Corps 1st Division headquarters. General Slocum had command of the 12th Corps by then.

Diven ordered our regiment to bivouac in a place where we could support the New York Battery Number One. The cannon boys began to set up by the white house and graveyard while our position lay in the skirt of the woods along a slight ravine to the left of the battery.

General Hooker himself came over during the evening and made fine speeches to the boys about what a great thing the 12th Corps had done, getting into our positions just so and all that, so that the next day we would beat Robert E. Lee when he come for us up from Fredericksburg. This was Hooker's strategy all along: to draw Lee out of the city and whip him in the hills where our superior artillery could get at him. He explained that the 11th Corps was set out behind us along the plank road to the west, in position to give us support when the enemy came our way. He had three Corps already there at Chancellorsville and five more Corps were on the way.

Everyone was whooping it up and congratulating each other but we four friends didn't think that our General Williams looked like a happy man. He stood to the side with his chin sunk to his chest like he did when he was thoughtful. I seen him that way plenty of times. We had grown to think the world of General Williams. He looked after us as best he could and took things cool. I knew for a fact he didn't like sleeping inside officers' quarters but preferred to sleep rough outside with us, sometimes not even in a tent but under a bush just like we had to do.

We had another officer we cared for a great deal, name of General Knipe. He was commander of the 1st Brigade of the 1st Division of our Corps. At Antietam he'd come through plenty for the 107th, helping our boys rally around the battery that was saved. I hadn't seen him do it that day on account of my head wound but I'd heard all about it.

His headquarters was back up the road a hop or two in an unfinished church building. He and General Williams were very close, fellow officers and friends. They stood together that night when Hooker rode up and down on his fine horse yelling out to the boys, "Our enemy must ingloriously fly or come out from behind his defenses and give us battle on our own ground!" We gave mighty cheers in response.

Knipe and Williams just walked away shaking their heads. I thought I knew what they were thinking: that Robert E. Lee would never "ingloriously fly," not never in a million years.

He and his two top boys, General Stonewall Jackson and General Longstreet, could be counted on to do exactly what you did not expect. Our boys did not call General Lee the "The Fox" for nothing!

We were sure tore up that night because we yearned to believe Hooker was right. We prayed that the war be over and done with so we could go home and get something to eat and get away from all the danger and misery of our situation.

At any rate, we passed an uneventful night with the exception of the occasional exchange of shots between the pickets and a certain foreboding of terrible events. We lay on our arms until dawn, alert and ready for immediate action.

1. The Chancellorsville House

Chancellorsville was just a crossroads where the Chancellor family had built a large brick house to house travelers on the turnpike. When Hooker claimed it as his headquarters, a female matriarch of the family and her 15 dependents were still living in it. They fled to a rear room of the house while the battle raged for the first day, then withdrew to the safety of the basement on the second of May, only leaving when the rebel cannon set fire to the house on the third day of battle.

Chancellorsville House, headquarters of General Hooker

Chancellorsville House after the Battle

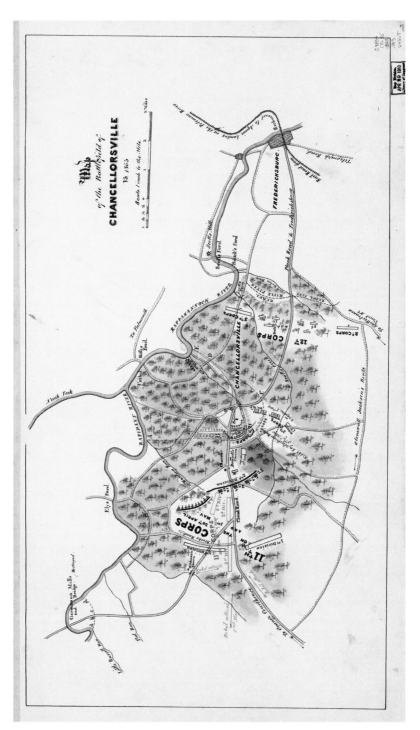

Map
of the Battlefield of
CHANCELLORSVILLE
Va 1863

Scale 1 inch to the Mile

Chancellorsville Map showing Jackson's Flank Attack

Chapter 15   Another Battle Begins

The next morning, May 1st, come upon us soft and quiet as any spring day ever did. General Williams sent us into the woods to chop down trees and build the crisscross fence works of felled trees they called abatis[1] for defense against the rebs. Then he went over to headquarters at the brick house to get orders for the day. He returned a little later empty handed. So he issued orders for us to continue to build the breastworks and to dig rifle pits just behind them. These were to extend all the way around the edges of our clearing in the borders of the woods.

I took a moment to pen a quick note to my parents.

I said, "In haste. I am well. We are ten miles from Fredericksburg and have cut off their supplies. Took two thousand prisoners yesterday. Got part of the rail road to Richmond. The troops are anxious to go on. We are going to clean them out certain. The whole Potomac Army are going to be engaged in the thing. We have got an awful grand army. Good bye, we are falling in."

I thought it might be the last words I might ever write to them.

The day grew hotter. Finally at noon the booming of cannons could be heard again from down river to the east.

So they marched us off in that direction, along the road toward Fredericksburg, to sweep the fields and woods clean of rebs as we went and push them backwards. We set off without complaint although we were exceedingly tired from the many days' marches we had made just getting there. We'd lately tramped over fifteen miles a day over hard roads with sixty pounds on our backs.

Our regiment was in the lead position. We came under almost constant artillery fire for two miles though the rebs didn't seem to be able to find our range and none of us suffered a scratch from shelling. The rebs got our tempers up tho and we started to get interested in a proper fight.

Just when it seemed like we were getting close to having one, a horse rode up all in a lather and we got new orders to return at once to Fairview. In that same moment we started to take more rifle fire. We returned it and might have kilt our first bunch of johnnies of the day. We wanted to keep at it but Wilkerson yelled out we had to go so we withdrew. There was grumbling in the ranks that the new order must surely be a mistake because we couldn't make any sense of it.

When we got back to Fairview things got more mysterious when we sent out our pickets all around the area and the ones to the south of our position encountered sharp conflict from a place no rebs were supposed to be. A general came over from the brick house to give further orders to Diven and while he sat upon his horse doing so, shells began to fall squarely amongst us. An enemy artillery battery on another hill had got the house in range and began to bomb us heavily.

I lay down next to our new captain, a man named Rutter who was very popular with all the men, being a very good fellow. He said to me, as a shell swished right over our heads, "Great Scott, Harnden, if they improve on that range a little, you and I are gone, certain!"

In a moment a shell came with its fearful song and struck the Captain. It completely tore the flesh from his back so that his spine and internal portions of his body were visible. Spattered with his blood, stunned and saddened, I tried to aid him but there wasn't nothing to be done. He was beyond help and died the next morning without ever coming to, a great loss to the regiment.

Another shell had pierced the chimney of the little house but we didn't know it at the time because of the racket of the artillery. It must've rattled right down and fell down in the ashes of the fireplace where it lay unexploded. Luckily for us, the next morning, the cooks made up their fires outside or General Williams told Wilkerson when they lit the fire inside, the shell would've certainly blown up and spoilt our breakfast.

When the barrage finally ended, we were able to go back to building the fences and digging rifle pits. We successfully extended our line of trenches all the way around the clearing through the trees and up to the plank road where General Knipe had his quarters. If the rebs came out of Fredericksburg from a southerly or easterly direction we'd certainly be ready for them now. The Division's many batteries of cannon were set up around Fairview pointing toward the fronts but we received no further assaults. The rest of the day passed in this fashion, without any confrontations.

Night came on quietly. Many of us sat up late, long after dark. From our high hillside we watched a big moon hang sparkling in the sky and the whippoorwills whistled and called to each other prettily. Only the very occasional rifle shot broke the peaceful spell of the place. I thought again of the strange tranquility of that night where we had laid out in the field of sweet clover before the terrible day at Antietam.

1. Abatis

Usually made up of trees, branches, or sharpened sticks, abatis were structures created to delay the progress of the enemy infantry of cavalry.

Chapter 16   May 2nd, 1863

Sometime in the early morning hours of that night, we thought we heard rumbling noises off to the south but we couldn't make out what they were in the faraway darkness. It seemed just an oddity, another of the mysterious side shows of war. How could any of us poor boys imagine what Robert E. Lee and old Stonewall Jackson was up to, busy as owls, quiet, swift, and clever. Those men must have been geniuses, if ever I saw one.

The sun broke slowly through a dense morning fog. We expected a big fight right away but again nothing happened. We had our breakfast at Fairview without the cooks getting blowed up by the shell in the farmhouse fireplace.

We still heard the far off noises from the south and more strangely still, additional rustlings from the west. On account of all the strange stirrings, General Williams went over to headquarters to express his misgivings. When he came back he told Wilkerson that he had been advised by Hooker that the enemy was in retreat!

Old Williams appeared to be greatly disturbed by this seemingly good bit of news. He gathered all our officers together and spoke with them at length. As was my habit, I stuck around trying to learn what was going on. Then I observed that he sent several trusted scouts out along the plank road, toward the 11th Corps from the direction whence we had originally come on the march from Kelley's Ford.

Sometime later the scouts returned with news that they had clearly seen signs of reb skirmishers or scouts moving in a large forested area directly to the west of us!

Now Williams and all the captains rushed immediately back to the brick house, expecting new orders forthwith.

But strangely Wilkerson come back with orders to take the Division out on the road to Fredericksburg like we done yesterday. "Gobble up the rebel rout," was how Hooker was said to have put it to our officers.

I wondered at that point if General Williams was a believer in this supposed retreat.

Diven told the regiment to throw off anything that would encumber us in the heat of the day and set out toward Fredericksburg at once. We done so and encountered very stiff resistance not two miles past the large brick house. Then I certainly did not think the rebs were demoralized and skedaddling, not one bit, nor did any of us. We threw ourselves on the ground and fought hard in that position for some time until another panicked horseman rushed up to order us back to Fairview in repeat of the very same action of the day before.

We retreated and marched as fast as we could back whence we had come.

When we got to our clearing, we suddenly beheld many rebel columns seemingly in retreat almost due south of our position there on the hill. Confused, but hoping for the best, we awaited further orders.

After what seemed too long a time to set still, new orders came from headquarters around three o'clock. We were given a double round of ammunition which amounted to 120 cartridges each and sent after the retreating rebs on the double quick.

We poured like a swarm of bees down into the woods and over a narrow roadway. Our regiment was to capture a reb battery which we supposed was stationed to protect the rear of the johnnies withdrawing columns. We marched bravely up to the cannons' mouth almost, falling on our faces occasionally to escape their shells.

Then suddenly, another horse covered in foam and nostrils distended approached bearing one of Hooker's officers. All in a terrible state of highest excitement, he screeched out orders to "Halt!

About face!" and race back to our old position because Stonewall Jackson had just flanked[1] our army from the western woods!

This revealed to us the fallacy of Hooker's theories and gave us such a shock as to quickly blanch our faces! This terrible error was one of the causes that led to the defeat of Old Joe Hooker's plans that day.

In a few moments we were flying along the route we had come, back towards our entrenchments. On our way, we suffered greatly from the shells of the enemy and the sharp shooters who were already perched in the tops of tall hemlock trees in the woods, some distance from the road. They picked off some of our officers as we come along.

Colonel Diven spied a reb in a large tree who had fired at him and almost got him. Diven called out a mere boy from our ranks who was considered a crack shot. He took the lad and pointed out the chap in the tree.

'Bang' goes the boy's gun and Mr. Johnny tumbled from that tree dead as a doornail.

As we come into our clearing at Fairview I almost had to stop running from the shock of what I saw was happening along the road and throughout the woods and fields. There was the wildest stampede of men, horses, wagons, tangles & such I ever saw rolling and churning, bearing down upon us to crush us like tiny ants. It was apparently the 11th Corp that had broke and was on the run. I seen right on these poor boys' heels were hordes of whooping rebs[2] tearing along with some of their clothes hanging off them in rags and tatters, looking and sounding like demons from the very depths of hell.

For a moment all was hysteria in our ranks except Old General Williams who kept a cool head and got the picture right quick. He ordered us and Knipe's Division to establish a line to flank that mighty stream of rebels. We gave a yell and a cheer of our own and within fifteen minutes we stopped the advance of those devils before they made it all the way to the Potomac Army headquarters at Chancellorsville House!

Later I heard that Stonewall was said to have poured out of those western woods with over twenty thousand rebs, every one of them screaming like a wild banshee. They had rolled up the whole poor unsuspecting 11th Corps like an old carpet and pushed it aside, yesterday's news.

As it was the rebs got within half a mile of General Hooker himself and all his unwitting staff[3]. Another General's bunch got the credit for stopping Stonewall's advance[4] but it was General Williams and us who did it for him. There wasn't another bunch there yet to see to the job at that point.

The minute we done it, Williams ordered us back to the Fairview clearing to regroup. We turned back but most of us couldn't get there on account of the 11th Corps still retreating and carrying some of us off in the mob. I had to fight through streams of men from my own side. By the time I made it back to the farm, there were less than a hundred men from the 107th there and not a friend of mine was evident among them. I had lost touch with my boys in the throng.

But luckily for us, with the reb advance now stopped cold, a lull in the fighting descended as the dusk came on. The johnnies thankfully seemed to be as disorganized and exhausted as we were. It just goes to show how even winning a battle will take it out of a man.

Soon the dusk gave way to darkness. Major Wilkerson thought there was quite a few reb troops on the north side of the road. We waited at the farm. Then orders came down from Hooker that we were to reform our ranks and advance back into the woods toward our entrenchments and rifle pits.

General Williams was furious at this order and tramped back and forth with General Knipe yelling that Hooker was crazy, but he knew he had to make us do it or get kicked out of the army and disgraced.

So the officers got back on their horses as we lined up again. Then they tried to march us into the woods. Immediately, as we entered there, a shadow of cold foreboding fell across my heart. Without Tenbrook, Edgerton or even Wiggins by my side my confidence faltered. It was horribly evident that none could tell who was who in the gloom beneath the trees. As General Williams had foreseen, it was so terribly confusing in there that most of the boys got lost within a few minutes. Though the full moon had come up again, the smoke from the battle made it glow a dull bloody red color which gave almost no light to see by.

Our old fool Diven tried to take us deeper in anyway. We crossed the ravine and formed another line in the edge of the woods, then we were to advance up toward the road till we found our old entrenchments and take possession of them. As we fell into a ragged formation, Diven realized that only two companies of men were still with him, mine and and one other, down to under thirty men I estimated. Frustrated, he joined us to the right side of a line of some of General Knipe's Division who said they were from the 128th PA. Then Diven left us and went back to find the others. He said he would be back shortly.

But Diven never did make it back into the woods.

We crouched in the dark and awaited further developments.

At long last, an officer did thankfully appear. Not Diven but General Knipe came, riding back and forth along his line. He ordered us to start slowly creeping up toward the plank road through the brush and trees. He issued strict orders not to fire out of fear that we might mistakenly shoot into our own men for all was unfathomable amidst the dense thickets and shadows.

A small group of five boys and I broke off from the rest when we found some of our old rifle pits to lay down in, as we'd been so ordered. We were then laying in an advanced position, in the left border of the woods by the road with men moving all around us in the dark and us not having the slightest notion who they were because of the tree trunks, limbs, bushes, and gloom that obscured or confused vision.

There was still no firing or shelling taking place at that point. I hoped to God there were no reb skirmishers or pickets close around us so we just laid low waiting, holding our breath.

A strange deep hush fell throughout the area and prevailed.

We could hear only the faintest sounds, axe blows chinking against wood from afar, the occasional muffled shout out, random voices echoing at distance in the forest. Some seemed to be behind us, some to the front.

Slowly it dawned on me that most of the voices had the telltale twang of those reb boys. Alarm ran high and higher amongst our little band. Occasionally a voice, nearer now, would cry out to inquire, "Who goes thar, be yer frind er foe?"

At one point I thought I heard our General Knipe calling for General Williams but faintly and too far off to be sure.

Feeling that we were becoming woefully unsafe where we were, I hoped we could make our way up to the road and get the heck out of there, for I feared we were becoming entrapped by our enemies. After a short spell and a confer we decided to leave the rifle pit and creep along up toward the plank road. We started and encountered not one of our own but heard more reb voices to all sides of us. It was then a cold chill ran down my back as I realized Knipe's lines must've pulled back and left us behind. If there had been orders to fall back, we had never heard them.

Imagine if you can the feelings of a soldier upon such an occasion. We were scared to death, as much of the horror of capture and the rebs' terrible Libby Prison as death. For prison and shame was worse than death to us soldier boys.

As we finally stumbled upon the plank road, I imagined for a moment we might find a safe route out of the dark trap of those woods, as there was still no shooting or cannon fire. The way looked open back toward Chancellorsville House, laying quiet in the dull red moonlight before us.

But as our fated luck would have it, just as we broke through the bushes alongside the road, I saw and heard a group of horsemen traveling on it, coming our way at a trot from a westerly direction. I judged for sure they were rebel cavalry, maybe a dozen men riding along in a strung out pack of shadows. They were nearing our position and closing the distance between our little band so rapidly as to produce within us a great deal of fear and panic.

Lost, disappointed, and desperate as I felt at that moment, my hopes for escape dashed, the tension and terrors of the night burst inside me and must have addled my wits. Barely knowing myself why I done it, I raised my rifle to my shoulder, took aim at the horsemen in the road, and let off a shot. I knew all the while it was strictly against General Knipe's orders.

My shot cracked out into the dark in a lonesome way, echoing through the night. For a moment it seemed that everyone around those parts froze listening to the sound of my gun as the echoes bounced amongst the trees and then died off. The riders in the road drew up their horses. No one moved.

Then slowly all hell began to unfurl as in some ghostly nightmare.

The boys I was with woke up and did the same thing as me, mostly also out of panic than any considered thought, sending five or six shots in a volley toward the horsemen.

Hearing the shots, the riders now reeled their horses around and galloped down the road from whence they'd come. I didn't know if we had hit any of them but it was as if my one shot had set off a veritable cascade of shooting as more rifle volleys commenced around us in the black woods.

The horsemen dodged here and there as the shooting continued and I heard excited yelling from many quarters, then came a mighty crash as if a whole regiment had let loose a volley. I watched as many of the riders went down, crashing along with their horses in the road some distance away.

After this exchange of gunfire, we expected to cetch it and we sure did. We ducked back into the bushes for cover as the road was immediately too dangerous but a crossfire caught us with bullets flying from both sides. Back in those infernal woods, we had no idea which way to go toward safety. As a group we fell to our knees and tried to get low enough to avoid the bullets flying every which way.

Suddenly a rider burst through the bushes. It was our noble General Knipe again, rode back for us, his horse jumping and dodging through the trees. I could only see him by the flashing of the musket fire.

He yelled for us to get out of there by order of, "Rise up, left face, and run for your lives!"

I tried my best to follow him as he dashed off but I didn't get far. I just couldn't make my way through the woods as an eruption of violence unleashed itself around me like a storm. I lost track of the men I was with and I felt it was every man for himself.

Now horses and men rushed every which way in the darkness, victims of the growing pandemonium. The sharp reports of rifle fire, the pinging and whistling of bullets, and the echoing of screams filled the air. Cannons began to add to the tumult, vomiting flashes of fire, the shells causing some of the woods to cetch on fire. I jumped and crawled along, searching for a way back to our clearing, any way out of the mayhem.

Suddenly I heard that old rebel yell from a thousand throats it seemed like, and in a moment a rebel wave of infantry was upon me.

I ran a few steps ahead of them, then tripping over a root in the dark and falling, decided on the way down to play possum rather than get myself killed. The reb boys rushed over me, one giving me a terrible whack with the stock of his rifle, remarking, "Here is one dead yank!" It took everything I had left inside not to jerk under the impact of his blow and betray my liveliness.

Another fellow stumbled over me, a number stepped on me, but I held my breath, praying none of them would reverse arms and plunge their bayonets through me.

I thought we yanks were whipped for sure but a few minutes later the rebel yell was lost in a mighty thunderous crash, the reverberating roar of large numbers of cannon opening fire. I knew they were our thirty-six guns at Fairview now swung in the right direction to attack the reb advance. Even though the shells, grape, and canister were rattling around me, and the limbs and foliage were falling on me, I felt some grim satisfaction that the rebs were going to cetch it now.

The rebs came rushing back and stumbled over me yet again.

They seemed to think I was a dead johnny not a dead yank and they didn't molest me this time. After they all passed I jumped to my feet and ran toward the sound of our guns and our lines like a madman. A happier soldier never lived than I when I broke out into the clearing and saw by the fitful glare of our flashing cannons the old Stars and Stripes. But just as I did, I heard the order from a yank gunner, "Double shot your guns boys and fire low!"

I dropped down in time to escape a broadside sent into the woods after the fleeing johnnies. Then I got up again and stumbled in amongst our batteries at Fairview. Some of those artillery boys would hardly believe that I come out of those woods alive. I hardly believed it myself.

I tried to join our new line of battle but all was still confusion. In the darkness we were hurriedly formed in line under strange officers without, for the time being, any effort at regimental organization. The officers urged us to be brave and to stand by the guns until every last one of us was shot down if necessary. It was as if the fate of the army depended on our holding this one position at Fairview.

To discourage us from running, officers and horsemen with drawn sabers were placed a short distance in the rear of the batteries with orders to "cut down" any snakes or cowards. Now and then a fearful whack of those sabers was heard as they fell upon the poor head of some fellow whose legs had tried to carry him off. I declare we were in as much danger from the rear as the front.

As the night wore on and it grew cold then colder still, the intense fighting died down at last, though the artillery fired their deadly missiles over our heads throughout the night. Utterly spent, we built fires, boiled up coffee and tried to attend to our wounded. They lay everywhere around us, inside and out of the farmhouse, moaning and crying out in their agonies. Medics arrived constantly to carry those that couldn't walk to the field hospital somewhere in our rear.

Miraculously, I found Tenbrook, Edgerton and Wiggins unhurt. We laid down together for a spell in an exhausted heap though we didn't get much sleep to speak of. I could barely speak to them of what had happened to me, I was that horrified and tired out. They told me they had never made it into the woods with Diven. He had later found them and taken a position with the remains of the regiment on the edge of the clearing during the battle.

By morning we knew our losses were beyond terrible. General Knipe's brigade was mostly cut to ribbons in the woods and he had lost all his officers save one. The whole 128th from Pennsylvania was entirely destroyed or captured. It came home to me over and over what an incredibly lucky man I was to have escaped with my life and make it back to the farm.

Never the less Williams ordered us to an early breakfast because he saw by first light¹ that Hazel Grove, a high clearing just south of us that used to be in our possession, was now held by reb artillery. He anticipated an attack at any minute and he was sure right. They soon opened fire and johnnies came at us once again out of those damnable woods.

What was left of our good old 107th was in another tight spot. We lay down on the hillside in front of the batteries and received fire for about one and a half hours as the enemy mounted wave after wave upon us. It seemed incredible that any of us lived through what we went through on that hillside in front of the Fairview Farm. Shot, shell and musket balls raked it incessantly.

The rebs made seven or eight desperate charges. In some of their charges, they would advance in three double columns, the first lying flat, the next kneeling, the third standing, and fire all at once, then charge with bayonets fixed. Their bullets flew around us like hailstones, most of us escaping by dropping low. Our gunners opened upon the rebs with grapeshot and canister and swept their ranks, piling up their dead in winnows.

1. The Flank Attack

Long before daybreak on May 2nd, while the two armies slept, Robert E. Lee sat down with Stonewall Jackson to hammer out a plan for the day's attack.

They understood exactly how General Hooker was trying to manipulate them into attacking him and they meant to outsmart him. Their last conference together was held at 2:30 am outside on a couple of cracker boxes set up beneath the dark trees. Speaking by flickering lantern light, they discussed the difficult challenges they faced.

Around them in the woods and fields lay over 150,000 heavily armed men, but only around 60,000 of that number were their own rebel fighters.

Furthermore their troops were ill supplied, tired to the point of exhaustion, and some had not seen a meal in days. Many a good general would have given in to the temptation to withdraw, perhaps to make a stand around Richmond where the army could be fed, but not these two. They had no intention of turning tail and running.

Both men knew their enemy well. They understood General Hooker's tendencies, as they had understood General McClellan's at Antietam. General Hooker wanted to bait them into attacking him, well they would attack, but only on their terms: a surprise attack, launched at just the right moment from a highly unlikely direction.

General Lee had earlier learned from his scouts and cavalry that General Hooker's right flank, the 11th Corps, composed of 11,000 men, was 'unsupported' as it lay stretched out in reserve along the Orange Plank Turnpike to the rear of the Union front. This was artfully called 'hanging in the air' in the Civil War vernacular, which meant that the 11th Corps did not have another Corps in position to protect it from a flank attack or otherwise come quickly to its aid if it got into trouble.

The two rebel generals decided that they must make the most of this weak place in the federal deployment, it was their only way of grasping the upper hand. Their conclusion was that they must take the risk of dividing their small force and that Jackson do something that seemed physically impossible.

He would move his whole corps of 28,000 men from their present position south of the federal lines. They would march quietly to the left, blatantly parallel to the Union front at first, and then he would take them on a long loop through the area called the 'Wilderness' that lay out to the west of Chancellorsville.

Then they would come back in a position to attack the 11th Corps, almost from behind. This Wilderness area was covered with second growth forest and dense underbrush. No one in his right mind would try to march a huge force of men on such a quick trip and expect them to make it, let alone be able to attack on the run directly afterwards. It was exactly the kind of idea the two Generals needed, one that was inconceivable to normal, some would say lesser, military minds.

Even General Lee was struck by the boldness of their plan at first. He asked Jackson if he was sure he could do it.

"Yes," replied Jackson decisively.

Lee gave Stonewall his blessing, secure in the knowledge that his friend would get the herculean task done or die trying. Lee had his own difficult work cut out for him. He would have to keep pressure on the huge Union front with a puny force of just under 30,000 men, banking on Hooker's plan to remain on the defensive and not figure out what was going on until it was too late.

That night a sympathetic local citizen was found to guide Jackson's columns on a narrow roundabout road through the dense acres of the Wilderness. All told, it amounted to a 12 mile march. It felt like 20 to his men.

It took them over 10 hours to cover the distance and many thousands of them would drop by the wayside from fatigue.

Starting at first daylight and throughout the coming day of May 2nd, Jackson and his thousands of men made the trip with his infantry screened by cavalry and various diversions thrown up to give the impression that he was retreating. Jackson even put a battery of cannon in the road south of the Fairview hillside to shoot at Fairview and make Hooker think it was to protect the rebel retreat. These are the cannons that Rufus and the 107th had to go try to capture.

Lee remained behind to make a show of attacking Hooker's front lines.

It was an incredibly daring gambit but they pulled it off.

In part they got away with it because Stonewall Jackson was like a force of nature, he just could not, or rather would not stop, and he inspired his men to persevere, no matter how awful the conditions. In part they got away with it because General Hooker simply did not believe the reports of strange enemy movements that filtered back to him during the day. He proclaimed the wilderness to the west to be absolutely "impenetrable." Hooker misinterpreted the evidence to mean that Jackson had seen the light, knew he was outnumbered, and was leaving the area, just as Jackson and Lee had hoped he would.

He did nothing to prepare for the terrible blow that was about to fall like a hammer on his unsuspecting right flank as it hung out in the air.

The 11,000 unfortunate soldiers of the 11th Corps on the Union right were cooking dinner and relaxing just after 5 o'clock in the afternoon, when out of the undergrowth came a burst of deer, rabbits, and foxes running in blind panic from something big that was moving in the thick woods behind them. The 'something big' soon proved to be a line three divisions deep and two miles wide of ragged rebels. There were 24,000 of them by all estimates, some 4,000 having fallen out from exhaustion on the grueling march.

The brambles and thickets had torn many of the rebs' uniforms to shreds. As they broke through the trees into the open, they began to run and whoop like the devil. The sight of them and the sound of the old rebel yell coming from over 20,000 throats pierced the hearts of the members of the 11th Corps and most of them turned around and began to flee for their lives.

The poor soldiers were taken entirely by surprise. Their day had seemed to be ending in perfect tranquility. They had been standing casually around their cooking fires in the fields, their rifles unloaded and stacked. The 11th Corps commander, General Howard, had been warned during the day to be on the lookout for a small attack from the West but he had stared into the tangled bushes of the Wilderness and decided not to take the threat very seriously. Now as the afternoon ended he had let his men almost totally drop their guard. Only 2 cannon were pointing at the woods, all the rest of his artillery was facing in the wrong direction, as was every entrenched position.

Within 10 minutes, a full blown rout enveloped the 11th Corps. Even the few who tried to make a stand to fight were swept away in the panic. Their mounted officers were shot down to a man. As the famished rebel infantry over ran the campsites and dodged among the cooking fires they only stopped long enough to reach down and gather up plates of food and hot cups of coffee.

The overwhelmed 11th Corps fell back in a wild stampede of men, tangled equipment, horses, and wagons all bearing down on the 12th Corps position around Fairview, like a floodwater filled with debris.

Some members of the 11th Corps ran so far that they passed Chancellorsville House through their own army lines to the east, and straight into the hands of the Confederates on the other side, asking desperately where they could find the road to the river and the pontoon bridges that might carry them home.

As General Williams and his Division had just then been called back to Fairview, they broke into the clearing and saw the enormous wave of retreating men, blind panic in their eyes, with a few surviving officers trying in vain to halt them, sometimes at the point of the sword. Coming fast on their heels were the nearly as hysterical rebels in their butternut rags, still whooping triumphantly at the top of their lungs.

2. Whooping Rebs

The rebel yell was a psychological weapon employed by the Southern side. It was a cheer and a battle cry all in one, by all accounts indescribably unsettling to the ears. "Woh-who-ey! Woh-who-ey! was one journalist's effort to get it down on paper. Many Southern units had their own slightly different version but basically it was an escalating, maniacal hoot that could carry for miles if enough men were doing it at the same time. It was used to curdle the blood of one's adversary in order to make him a less effective fighting man. It reportedly worked remarkably well.

William Russell, a war correspondent for The Times, a Northern newspaper, wrote, "the southern soldiers cannot cheer, and what passes muster for that jubilant sound is a shrill ringing scream with a touch of the Indian war-whoop in it."

The origins of the yell were most likely a combination of many factors. The three main theories are 1) that it came from the hunting and fighting cries of Scottish highlanders from the British Isles whose ancestors predominated among the settlers of the South. 2) That it was an imitation of Native American war cries, hence the whooping effect, and 3) that it was an approximation of the yelps of the hounds that were used extensively in the South to track and hunt down raccoon, fox, and runaway slaves.

Some of the power of the rebel yell, aside from its general creepiness, derived from the sense that if you were hearing it come in your direction, then you could count on the fact that you were being hunted by a bunch of men who had every intention of doing you harm of the most serious nature if they caught you.

3. Hooker and His Unwitting Staff

Ironically, General Hooker and his staff at the Chancellorsville House were some of the last federal officers to realize that they were being flanked by General Jackson directly from the West. It seems the area around the large brick house was in what is called an "acoustic shadow." Technically this is a place where waves of sound are disrupted and blocked either by the topographical features of the landscape such as trees or hills, or by the wind. Though the sounds of the rout were clearly heard many miles away by others, the officers at the house enjoyed the last rays of afternoon sunshine undisturbed. Whatever caused the acoustic shadow at Chancellorsville House, it is said that General Hooker and his aides were actually relaxing on the porch, utterly ignorant of the sad plight of their 11th Corps. Eventually they could detect cannon firing somewhere off in the distance but they could not tell where it was coming from. At last a captain grew uneasy, stepped down off the porch and used his field glasses to search the countryside. As his gaze fell to the west, he saw the great wave of men approaching along the road and through the fields. He cried out in alarm, "Great God! Here they come!" Hooker and his staff immediately jumped on their horses and rushed in the direction of the melee, much too late to do anything about it.

4. General Williams' Counter Flank Attack

When General Williams saw the rebel flank attack and the fleeing 11th Corps, he knew what he had to do: he must stop the rout if he possibly could before it reached the army central headquarters at the Chancellorsville House, less than half a mile away from his position.

He took 2 brigades from his division, Knipe's and Ruger's, which included Rufus and the 107th, and went to establish a battle line that could flank the rebels as they advanced. He reported that his men charged bravely into the woods with a yell and a cheer of their own and were able to check the rebel advance within 15 minutes. General Williams was extremely proud of his men for their work in stopping the flank attack, something another Corps, the 3rd, was ultimately given credit for in the newspapers back home.

He later wrote in an indignant letter to his daughter about this: "This is the true story of the first checking of Jackson's pursuit of the 11th corps. The New York papers are giving immense glory to General Sickles of the 3rd Corps for this very act. But he was at least 2 miles away and did not get back to the vicinity of this affair till some time after dark...and it was the 1st Division, 12th Corps, which stopped an exulting enemy pursuing a disorganized and broken corps and which had reached within half a mile or less of the headquarters of the commander of the army!"

Stonewall Jackson's flank attack had luckily lost some of its forward momentum right around the time Williams sent his brigades to stop it. The rebel regiments, having just carried out a 12 mile march and an extended attack on the run for two miles, were exhausted and in a state of disarray themselves. In addition to the the day's taxing march through the Wilderness and the pace of the attack itself, the 2 mile wide battle lines had been funneled down to several hundred yards in and on either side of the Orange Turnpike road. The rebel advance ground to a halt just to the west of Fairview from overcrowding and disorganization as well as from the 12th Corp's counter flank attack.

After the rebel attack was halted General Williams got further orders to advance again. Knowing this to be extremely foolish General Williams protested but was told that the order to go back into the woods had come directly from General Hooker himself and must be carried out immediately.

Unfortunately, what ensued was exactly what Williams had feared. His men could not tell friend from foe and chaos soon prevailed in the darkened woods. They were easily flanked in the dark.

Though there was almost a full moon that night and the skies were clear, the battle smoke had dulled the moonlight to an eerie, reddish color that offered only the slightest visibility.

As Williams said later, referring to the moonlight, there was "just enough of its light to make darkness visible."

Colonel Diven tried to follow the orders and took some of the 107th NY into the woods but as Rufus reported, most of them got lost. Diven then went looking for the rest of his lost regiment. He found them "broken in fragments." Eventually he was able to locate most of them but he did not attempt to send them out to the lines forming in the woods. Instead he had them lie down under cover at the edge of the woods with the other disoriented men from Williams' Division and wait out what happened next. He judged there was just no point in trying to do anything else under the circumstances. There was no gunfire in the area for some time at this point, in spite of how close the enemies got to each other around the barricades. Officers did not permit their men to fire at the various stirrings around them in the dark trees for they could not tell who they would be opening fire on. Then, As Robert Krick put it in 'The Smoothbore Volley That Doomed the Confederacy,' "A swarm of Federals had by accident curled up between the outer skirmish line, manned by the 33rd North Carolina, the (rebel) regiment farthest to the right in Lane's main line. Most of the disoriented Northerners belonged to the 128th Pennsylvania." Some other accounts mention a small band of lost federals. "There was a single shot fired...in an instant it was taken up, and nearer there were five or six shots...and then suddenly a large volley, as if from a Regiment." David Kyle, corporal and Stonewall Jackson's guide the night of May 2nd, 1863.

General Knipe, who saved Rufus's life at Chancellorsville

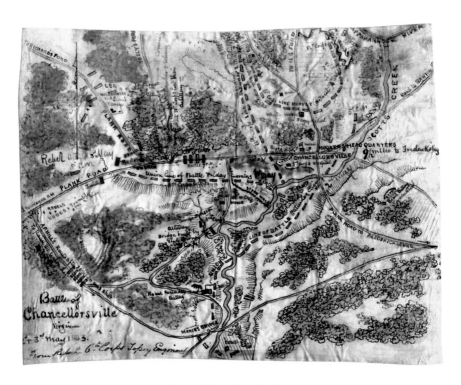

Map of Chancellorsville Battle

Chapter 17   May 3rd, 1863

The terrible battle was hard work and it made our blood run cold to hear the screams of their wounded and dying. In places, their dead completely covered the ground. But the rebs kept coming on so strong that finally we had to stand in order to save our cannons. The johnnies were constantly reinforced, out numbering us in infantry.

Orders came from Hooker to "Hold our position at the farm if every man is shot down!"

There ran a kind of hysteria amongst us. Fellows would jump to their feet and scream and holler threats while brandishing their weapons, even sometimes laughing in the face of death.

Within a short while I had fired some sixty rounds. Our old flag was felled once more to the ground. Diven now rushed up with sword drawn and savagely ordered the sergeant of the color guard to "Up with those colors!" The sergeant replied that he could not as the staff was shot off.

"Well," screams the brave old Colonel, "Up with what is left of them or I'll cut your head off!" The sergeant struggled to his feet and held up the flag by the edges like to make his body into a staff. The sergeant did not live long in that position.

We kept rising to our knees to fire our guns until we was mostly shot down or out of ammunition. I fired right into their ranks which were ten rods from us. Several bullets soon made holes through my clothes.

Then my bullet jammed in my gun so I threw it down and picked up another that was lying there but my ammunition wouldn't fit it, for it turned out to be a rebel gun. I threw that gun down too and took mine back up to try to clear the thing. I put in my wormer and was able to get the jam cleared. I went at it again, taking aim, firing away and just getting interested when a bullet struck my belt from the side, the force of it knocking me over but not hurting me.

I'd just got myself back up onto my knees when something thudded and clinked against my gun barrel though I didn't feel a thing but a sort of shock in the grip of my hand.

I was knocked flat once again. Rolling over, I looked down and seen a lead ball had went through between the first two knuckles of my left hand and flattened out against the gun stock tearing apart the flesh of my palm and most likely breaking some small bones along the way.

With difficulty but little pain, I rose and tried to resume firing. The first ball I attempted to ram home stuck fast at the same point where it had stuck before. I attempted to dislodge it with my wormer but didn't succeed. I picked up a dead comrade's gun and fired a few more rounds but the wound began to pour out so much blood I had to wrap it tight in my gun rag to stop it. It was then that I was ordered to the rear by a medic.

I hated to abandon my friends in such a fearsome place but I did not think that I could use my hand and be of any further use to them. I began to make my way in a low crouch to the rear of our lines, leaving Tenbrook and Edgerton and firing away like men possessed. Wiggins seemed to have disappeared, swallowed up in the chaos.

Once I got to where I deemed it safer to stand, I walked along for a mile and a half right behind our troops that were fighting and getting cut down at an awful rate. The bullets flew there as badly as they did at the front but I was spared.

I joined a little band of non combatants by reason of wounds. As we started back towards the hospital there were about fifteen of us.

On our way we went through more batteries around the Chancellorsville house. I saw groups of men standing among apple trees in an orchard, the whole of them thrown into the air by a shell bursting in their midst. I was almost in as much danger from the flying debris and mules as from the shells. Dead horses and artillery were piled up in heaps on every side. Once again, as at Antietam, the gore was beyond description. Turning from the sickening scenes we continued on when a shell struck one comrade between the shoulders, rolled him over and over upon the ground like a ball, and crushed out his life. I took his hand in his death agony. We left his crumpled body and hurried on along the northern border of the field.

When we arrived at the big brick house, General Joe Hooker[2] was standing there, cool as a cucumber. We stopped to watch the goings on.

All the generals and other officers were riding up to him to get their orders when the reb cannons started knocking the big house all to pieces behind him. He stood by not flinching a muscle as he gave out orders to his excited staff. One of his orderly's horses was killed within three rods of Hooker but he never even looked around. Not moving a muscle he stood with his field glass steadily to his eye as if utterly unaware of the danger to himself. Then he mounted his horse and he and his aides rode off into the thickest part of the fray.

We boys were so impressed with his grand courage and splendid bearing that we were silent in rapt admiration and for the moment forgot our own peril and pain.

Then we went on another ways[3] to our hospital tents in the woods by the river. They couldn't help us as they were packing up and leaving as fast as they could for fear the rebs would shell them soon. By that time I had come across another seven or eight wounded men from my regiment. We went on back to the river together, crossed it on the pontoon bridge and went up toward the bigger Corps hospital there, thinking we were finally out of danger. But not so. There came a great swish as a shell struck among our little band. It threw us in every direction. I was able to get up and run a few more steps but then I fell stunned and had to crawl the rest of the way.

When I reached the hospital, the doctors kindly removed the jagged bullet from among the bones of my hand but told me they would have to amputate the most of it to save my life. They said to sit tight and await my turn on the operating table. I'd seen enough of amputations and all they entailed for one lifetime, thank you very much. The thought of trying to go through life without the use of my hand was a terrible thing to me. I studied the wound and decided I might try to save the limb without any further attention from those sawbones. I lined up the bones and pieces of flesh, wrapped it up tight in a cleaner cloth, and tucked my arm inside my blouse for a sling.

After that, I chose to walk away from that place against the doctors' orders, taking my own french leave of them. I finally sank down upon the ground utterly spent and was senseless for about fourteen hours, even when some boys kindly moved me into a tent.

I awoke to what was my seeming fate of dodging shells again. At daybreak one came crashing through the canvas over my head, followed by another and another in quick succession. I was so terrified that for a moment I couldn't move. Then I sprang out of that tent pretty lively and in my terrible fright, ran off through the woods, all the while still in range of the shells.

All at once a scene loomed up before me that completely broke me up and I was in actual danger, I think, of dying of sudden fright. There was a mob of yelling rebs confronting me, maybe seven or eight thousand in number. I sank down upon the ground limp and helpless before I became aware they were prisoners. They were carrying on most boisterously over what they hoped and supposed was an attack on that side of the river meant to rescue them.

Then I recovered my wits and made my way by the rail cars with what was now mobs of walking wounded to Acquia Creek where I saw another man I knew from the regiment. He told me how I could get to Washington and I started off again. Through him, I found the steamer that was loading casualties bound for Washington. I was a sorry mess by that time. My clothes, what was left of them, were saturated with blood and my face blackened by gunpowder. On deck, I dropped off into a slumber so deep they had trouble awakening me when we arrived at the wharf in Washington the next day.

There I was placed in an ambulance wagon and taken to a place called Campbell Hospital[4]. This was a simple barracks of one story, whitewashed inside and out, but decorated with gay paper, evergreens, and fragrant with the smell of flowers. The beds were clean and inviting. The ladies of the Sanitary Commission were present to look after us. That hospital was the most delightful place I had ever beheld in my life. I stripped off my tattered clothing and sank down onto a bed, astonished that once again I had survived such an ordeal but sick at the thought of the plight of my friends and all the other tried and true boys of the 107th NY regiment.

1. The Third Day of Battle

Before daybreak, General Williams had ordered his men of the 1st Division to breakfast without delay.

He feared an early attack with the coming light when he found out that a high clearing just south of Fairview called Hazel Grove, previously held by the Union 3rd Corps Artillery, was now occupied by rebel batteries.

During the night, General Hooker had decided to withdraw his front lines into a tighter more defensible formation. In doing so, his own artillery forces had given up the crucial clearing on the hill at Hazel Grove. Now, a rebel general named Stuart had set up 30 guns there. Williams was right, Stuart's cannon's soon began to shell the 12th Corp's position while rows of rebel infantry attacked them from the woods.

The 107th lay down in the edge of the woods and received incoming fire for about one and a half hours. Then they were ordered to advance into the open to the aid of a regiment that was reportedly surrounded. General Williams summed up his Division's ensuing experiences this way:

"It seemed a wonder that anything could live on that slope and hill-brow in front of Fairview. Shot and shell and musketry swept it from end to end and side to side, and the columns of destructive missiles seemed to increase every moment." In all, the terrible fighting on the hillside lasted for 4 hours.

2. General Joe Hooker

When Rufus saw General Hooker as he sat upon his horse so admirably unafraid and issuing orders in the midst of the shelling at the Chancellorsville House, the General was actually practically incapacitated at the time.

Just before Rufus came along, Hooker had been standing on the porch looking through his field glasses when a cannonball hit the support column right next to him. He was blown off the porch, not seriously injured but was terribly stunned and concussed, so much so that his staff got the addled General on his horse and took him to get medical attention.

Hooker reluctantly turned responsibility for the army over to his second in command, a general named Couch, for the rest of the day.

Later this event would give Hooker an excuse for some of the failures of leadership that occurred during the battle.

3. After Rufus Left the Field

Around the time that Rufus was wounded and left the the front lines to start his dangerous journey back to the hospital, General Williams was notified that all the regiments under his command were running out of ammunition and could not hold Fairview any longer without support.

He sent an officer to General Hooker at the brick headquarters, requesting supplies and fresh troops as he feared his men were near the point of complete exhaustion. The concussed Hooker had left the area but an officer on his staff told Williams' man that he should tell Williams to somehow magically supply his men with ammunition and relief himself, even though Williams knew that Hooker had many fresh regiments held back in reserve along the North Road to the river fords. Left entirely to his own devices, Williams described what happened next.

"There was no time for delay if I would save anything of my command. Oh! But for one of the four corps which lay behind me unengaged. But I do not intend to express opinions. I am giving facts. The getting away was worse than the staying. Our line of retreat was over the ravine, up an exposed slope, and then for 3/4 of a mile over an open plain swept by artillery and infantry of the Rebels as they pressed forward. There was no shelter on our side of Chancellorsville House, and no reinforcements appeared to stay the pursuers...Many a poor fellow lost his life or limb in this fearful transit."

Once Williams and his Division reached the general headquarters at the brick house he was commanded by Hooker's remaining staff to halt his retreat and hold the place at all costs. When Williams replied that he had no ammunition left, one of the staff officers directed him to "Use the bayonet!"

Williams pointed out that they were for the most part being bombed from a half mile away, rendering the suggested use of their bayonets completely ridiculous. In total disgust, he rode back to his command.

William's growing frustration resulted in his later, bitter note in his journal, "I knew the 1st, 2nd, 5th, and 11th corps were within a mile to

3 miles of us and yet here my poor devils were ordered to suffer, after a fearful conflict which had in reality kept them under arms all night and in which they had expended 80 rounds of ammunition per man."

Soon the Chancellorsville House was set on fire by the rebel shells as were the woods around it. Unable to hold the ground, Williams ordered his men to continue their withdrawal up the road to the north until they arrived at a white house where they met the 2nd Corps who were just now moving up to the front to meet the rebels, several hours too late.

Williams formed his division in a line to the rear of the 2nd Corps, then he allowed the men to fall out and rest at long last. Riding his horse out through the confusion and smoke of the battlefield, Williams found a stray team of pack mules, deserted by their drivers, whose wagons still contained some ammunition. He led the train back to his troops and was able to replenish their ammunition.

The fighting seemed to diminish somewhat after General Williams ordered his men to take their rest on the ground.

They sat there for many hours, surrounded by the sounds of the battle but thankfully spared an actual engagement. After dark they were sent to a new, safer position above the river on two bluffs.

What was left of Williams' 1st Division lay down beneath some evergreen trees and slept soundly for the first time in several days. In the 107th NY, of the 225 men who had begun the fight on May 1st, 98 were now dead, wounded, or unaccounted for. Rufus was wounded, Wiggins was missing, and Tenbrook and Edgerton were safe. Wiggins turned out to be uninjured and was able to find and rejoin the regiment in the next several days.

By the end of that fateful Sunday, the 4th of May, 1863, Hooker had allowed his huge army to be contained and whipped by Lee's much smaller force. Now the only way open to the survivors of the Army of the Potomac was the humble road leading back to the US Ford across the Rappahanock River.

The morning of May 4th brought much cooler temperatures to the men still departing the battlefield. The 107th NY took their place in line to cross the river and then waited for many long cold hours near the U S Ford. Around 3 o'clock, there was a big thunderstorm followed by a steady rain that chilled them to the bone. They continued to wait patiently, building big campfires to warm themselves up to a livable temperature.

finally General Williams went to see what the delay was about and was told that the rain had washed out all 5 of the pontoon bridges.

Again, they stood around for several more hours in the rain as 2 bridges were put back up by army engineers. Enemy artillery fire kept up an ominous booming in the south that moved inexorably in their direction. The Division was almost the last to cross the river and begin their retreat back into Union territory. They marched directly to Stafford Courthouse in one final long, hard march and made camp. "And so," said General Williams, "ended the last day's campaign in Dixie."

Williams reported that his final numbers were of 31 field officers engaged, he had lost 14. All his adjutant generals were wounded or missing. Of the 5000 troops Williams had in Sunday's battle, he had lost 1700, or one in three. However he had not lost one single piece of artillery. A fact he was deservedly very proud of.

4. Campbell Hospital

When Rufus arrived in Washington after the battle, one of the greatest changes in the city since he had last been there was the enormous growth in the number of hospitals. At the beginning of the war, the city was home to just one medical facility, now in 1863, there were over 50 establishments dedicated to the care of injured soldiers. Some were very small clinics in private homes or churches and some were huge new hospitals built recently out of necessity.

The biggest and most famous were The Armory Square, The Campbell, and The Finley Hospitals.

Campbell was in the outskirts of the city, out on 7th Street. Previously a barracks for cavalry, it now had spaces for 600 beds in a number of long white, one story buildings called pavilions. It was one of the few city hospitals that was connected by pipes to the Potomac River so that relatively fresh water flowed continuously to it and was taken away by drains. Some of the wards even had indoor bathrooms and sinks with running water, something that Rufus had not seen before. The level of hygiene was much higher that in the other hospitals, simply due to the advantage of a constantly refreshed water supply.

Chapter 18   Campbell Hospital

In the days following the battle, the doctors argued and argued that I must let them take my hand off. I stuck to my guns and would not relent for anything. It was puffy and tattered but I did not think it had contagion in it yet. I told them I had some medical training and would use it to care for my own wound.

There was no news from the front. I worried constantly about the boys and the tight spot I had last seen them in. We only heard that the 12th Corps was nearly destroyed. I wrote immediately to my parents that I was alive and some details of the battle, that Antietam now seemed a skirmish by the side of it.

I thought it was on account of we were whipped so bad that Old Joe Hooker wouldn't allow news about the army or the battle to be put into the newspapers. The slaughter was so terrible that the steamers ran day and night on the river bringing the wounded into Washington.

My prayers began to run toward the doctors sending me home while my hand was lame. It had been a long while since I had enjoyed the benefit of Christian society and I longed for it, as well as the comforts of home and family. I couldn't see that I would ever make it back to the regiment and thought maybe if not sent on furlough I could find a job in the hospital to do and stay on there working for the doctors or in the drugstore.

Campbell was a very kindly place. They gave us good victuals, washed us regular, and kept everything nice, neat as a pin. There were even some washing rooms where water flowed through pipes right in to use without anyone having to haul it. They told me the water come direct from the Potomac. The only thing I really wanted there was the consent of the surgeons to spare my hand. I finally got it, tho they said I ran the risk of losing my life.

I told them I would take the chance and that I was content to put myself in God's hands.

My hand was further cleaned and bound up by the hospital nurses and I thought it might heal all right with maybe just the loss of use in a couple of fingers if it didn't get the gangrene into it and fester.

It began to rain something fierce in Washington and lasted for several days. I felt awful bad for all the men still laying out on the battlefield. I thanked God everyday for my good luck to be somewheres indoors.

We finally heard news by dispatch that Hooker had surrounded the rebs after all and they were on the verge of surrender. I felt excited and patriotic again for a half a minute but then word came through that we were terribly whipped after all, and by a piddling army only half our size. We also heard that our good Brigadier General Gordon might have been killed, among many other officers, including the sergeant who had taken Tenbrook's place away from him.

Of my friends, I still had not one word and I worried about them constantly. After some days, I was rested enough to get out of my bed and I began to walk about the place to search for them. There was not one other of the 107th in my ward at Campbell, but I feared our regiment was cut to pieces.

There were thousands of men there to be cared for, some of them very bad and dying off. They piled the dead on carts and hauled them away like so much firewood. I seen the carts passing by our windows several times a day. Where had they all come from? I wondered. How many family circles were now broken forever? Each one of those poor souls had been somebody's darling child.

But on the plus side, there were also many very good men and ladies to help us in that place. I liked my doctor, named Dr.

True, especially. He said he would try to get me a furlough if he could. I didn't know if he could do it as he wasn't head man at the hospital. So far, there was no sign of contagion or black matter in my wound. I reflected that perhaps since no dirty material from my uniform had been driven into it by the ball, it was easier to clean than many wounds the boys suffered.

One day Old Abe the President himself come through to stop at folks' beds and tell us thank you for our sacrifice. The ladies gave him a large bunch of flowers from the gardens they kept on the hospital grounds.

Around about the 15th of May, we heard the startling news that Old Stonewall Jackson was dead from wounds suffered at the battle. I could hardly believe such a man could be kilt off. The papers said the whole South[1] was taken over with grief and worry. They did not know how General Lee could ever fight the war out to success without his right hand man.

Us boys in the field knew no one could have stopped Stonewall. We none of us yanks ever had been able to manage it. And he had sure outsmarted us at the battle, marching all his boys through the wilderness night and day and coming at us sneaky like he done. Throwing us off by giving the appearance of a withdrawal. He had fooled us one and all, except of course for wise old Williams. I now judged that our own good General Williams was onto Stonewall's shenanigans before any other officer in the whole Union army.

I felt deeply aggrieved about Stonewall, for he was a man us soldier boys loved and respected from a distance. He was the most Christian general there ever was and always sought to obey God's higher laws was how I saw it, even if he was on the wrong side of the thing. He was truly the most honorable and best general they had, certainly even that we had. Any number of men would have laid down their own lives for such a man. I know I felt that way, and he was supposed to be my enemy. All the boys felt so about Stonewall.

We heard no details of his killing but I couldn't imagine how it had happened as usually the high generals were so well protected from harm.

The newspapers said his body was taken down to Richmond to lie in state so that the vast crowds of mourners could come by and pay their last respects. It seemed to me the whole country was sorry for the loss of that noble man, even regular folks in the North expressed that sentiment due to their high regard and admiration for him.

Each day I walked through the wards looking for boys I knew. I found a few from the regiment and began to sit with some others. I witnessed so many scenes of tragedy and misery in that place. There were citizens[2] who came during the long days just to set a spell with each patient because that is what our boys needed the most, a little company and another soul to talk to. Sometimes it made all the difference.

Near my own bed was a young boy who was wounded at Fredericksburg and had his arm taken off. The job was done poorly and he had not been well since. Even lacking an arm, they had put him back in his regiment to fight again. When he went into the battle at Chancellorsville it wore him out. He came here a day or two after I did. I took a good deal of interest in him, getting things that would taste good to him & such. I also wrote his letters for him.

Well, then, one day, I made up my mind that he could not live long, but I did not tell him so. He called me to his bedside and said he felt death coming on and he wanted me to write something to his wife. He wanted her to become a Christian and meet him in heaven. He said he had been very wicked but repented of it. I think he was prepared to die.

The day after that he seemed better and everyone said so. I had gotten a pass to go into the city and see some sights so I said goodbye and started off but I thought the boy might be as my friend Decature was back in camp with the fever, when he had no feeling of pain about him just before the end. And so it proved. When I came back in the afternoon, the boy's bed was empty. They said he died a short time after I started for the city. The death of a comrade was such a common occurrence, since I had been in the service, that it didn't even seem like death anymore. But in this case, I felt different from what I ever done before, except for when my friend Decature died back at Harpers Ferry.

I read the lists of the wounded in the papers and found no mention of any of my friends so I concluded they were most likely safe and staying with the regiment over at Stafford Courthouse where I heard it lay, licking its wounds I imagined. I also heard that General Knipe was down so sick with malaria and so discouraged that he went home to be nursed by his wife in Pennsylvania. And that General Williams was almost broke down himself but as there were no other officers left to care for the Division he had to stay on with no chance at a furlough home.

You could not imagine the feelings a soldier in the hospital had when he got his furlough. It seemed like a man at home getting a gift of four or five thousand dollars, it made them that happy. Some fellows would get one brought to them and they would jump right up from their bed and start for the depot without a moments delay. My own chances for a furlough never seemed to play out, probably because my hand was healing well enough that they wanted to send me back to the regiment soon. I thought I deserved one but I did not get it. I had to stand it as I had stood other disappointments.

1. The Whole South Was Taken Over with Grief and Worry

Reaction to Stonewall's death amounted to a flood of dismay that broke over the Southern states. It was as if a piece of the soul of the rebellion had died, leaving an empty place that ached painfully and could not be filled by any other general or political figure.

Many Southerners felt that their rebellion was doomed to eventual defeat without the great tactical and spiritual example that Stonewall set with his unfailing ability to win out over seemingly impossible difficulties. Whether it would prove to be a self-fulfilling prophecy or not, the Confederacy did lose the next big battle in the eastern theater, at Gettysburg, Pennsylvania, in early July of 63, and go on to eventually lose the war.

2. Men and Ladies to Help Us

In addition to the large staff of army doctors, medics, and nurses who took care of Rufus and his fellow casualties, many volunteers of both sexes came forward to work as aides in the Civil War hospitals. President Lincoln himself visited the Washington wards as often as he could to comfort and thank the patients for their service and sacrifice. It was during these frequent visits that he was given bouquets of flowers from the gardens on the grounds.

Of the volunteers, the most famous, apart from Red Cross founder Clara Barton, was the poet Walt Whitman, from Long Island, New York. He was over 40 when the war began and did not enlist due to his age, but his two younger brothers did. When one of them was injured at Antietam, Whitman, fearing the worst, travelled from New York to Falmouth, Virginia to tend to him in a field hospital. He was so moved by the plight of the wounded men he saw there that when his brother recovered, Whitman went on to Washington and began to spend his time administering to patients in the Armory Square and Campbell Hospitals. He called himself a "psychological nurse" and tried to provide what the overworked doctors could not, namely tender companionship and perhaps most importantly, hope.

He later wrote that, "The doctors tell me I supply the patients with a medicine which all their drugs & bottles & powders are helpless to yield." While he worked in the hospitals, Whitman was commonly observed to be filling a series of small notebooks with notes, impressions, and bits of poetry. After the war, he used these resources to assemble a book of poetry called "Taps" about his experiences in the Washington wards. 'Taps' is one of the most powerful of all the first person wartime accounts of the grim toll that the Civil War took on human beings, especially the many who survived the initial battles, only to come back to fight other, more personal battles for health and survival. In addition to the private citizens who staffed the hospitals, help came from two commissions that had been formed to supply the soldiers and hospitals with the many things the US government could not afford to buy. They were called the Sanitary and the Christian Commissions. Both were private organizations that were funded through donations, raffles, and other money raising efforts held throughout the North.

Campbell Hospital in Washington, D.C.

Ward in the Carver Hospital, Washington

Clara Barton, founder of the American Red Cross

Walt Whitman, poet

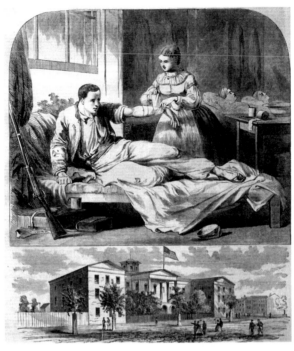

Nurse Tending to Wounded Soldier

Wounded Soldiers after Chancellorsville

Chapter 19   Hospital Scenes

Soon after I arrived at the hospital news came in that our General US Grant had finally taken Vicksburg out in the western theater of the war. This time I thought the good news might actually be true but once again it turned out to be rosy. What was true was that General Grant had begun to lay a siege on that city and planned to wear them out till they were starved and gave up.

Personally I wanted Mac to come back and take over the army again. Maybe we didn't exactly beat the rebs when he had charge over us but at least they didn't whip us neither. All the boys in the army wished it so. Some wounded reb boys I knew in the hospital said that if only we would keep Mac out of the field, they could hold their own without Stonewall.

Then my father came down sick at home and letters from my family faltered. My mother worried so that I tried to buck her up with word that I was mending fast and getting fat too, which was mostly truthful. What I didn't tell her was that living in a hospital was where one long sad scene played out after another and my spirits sometimes grew so heavy I had to work hard to tote them around with me.

Sometimes a mother or a sister would come to see their wounded son or brother, who was injured as to not be able to leave his bed. They would look at each other, and not a word said, but down the ladies would go onto the floor or the nearest bed fainting in shock and grief. I witnessed all sorts of scenes there.

I brought one old lady to see her son. While she was with him he had his leg taken off and afterwards the doctor told her that her boy couldn't live very long. The old lady watched by him as none but a mother could, night and day, her face bathed in tears all the while. But you may ask what made her feel so bad when she knew he couldn't live. I'll tell you why. It was she came expecting to find her three sons here, but found out by this one that the other two were shot dead in the battle.

This last surviving son, knowing that his parents were poor, begged his mother to let him be buried here at the soldiers' home. He tried every which way to console her, but when he died, she had to be carried away, she was that distraught. I felt so sorry for the poor woman.

With very few letters & such from my family, I felt further discouraged. Those letters were like a lifeline to me from back home where things were sensical and familiar. I had seen fellows ruint in that way more than anything else. Their folks at home didn't write to them and they got to thinking that they were not thoughten anything of by their folks. They would have nothing to restrain them and they would drink and be in the guard house all the time. If they got a furlough, they wouldn't go home, but instead would go off somewhere on a spree.

Finally the doctors came around to our ward to make out our certificates and descriptives and decide who would get a furlough. They made out papers for two or three to get theirs. Then the head surgeon Dr. Baxter, happened to come in.

He says to me, "Let me look at your wounds."

He looked, then told me I couldn't have my papers made out, and he went off (the rascal!). I could have chawed Old Baxter's head off. So I wouldn't be getting home for awhile, if ever. If they had offered me a furlough at that moment, I wouldn't have taken it, I was that mad. I swore that someday I would pay him off for it.

At the end of May I finally got a letter from Tenbrook. He and Edgerton were with the regiment at Stafford Courthouse. Wiggins had turned up at long last having been gone off again for awhile since the third day of the battle to who knows where. They told me that a lot of the boys were getting sick again and lying all around in their tents suffering with fever. I never knew a regiment to have such luck.

Tenbrook thought they might be headed out soon for another big fight with General Lee. They were scared to go in again under Joe Hooker tho. At the hospital we considered that he was a noble man but in the field the boys had seen too much of him and wished for a man with a better head and not one to puff himself so much. Since I had seen him on the hottest part of the battle field I still thought I never saw a braver man, nor read of one.

By June 7th, I was healed up well enough that I found the doctors were to give me a real job. The feeling had returned to the fingers of my injured hand so much so that I could use it for lighter tasks. They appointed me to Head Clerk[1] in the hospital drug department, so in a way it turned out to be lucky I did not get that furlough.

It was much like my place in Waverly, that is, it was an apothecary's shop. I would have about the same to do as I did at the one at home. The pay was only thirteen dollars a month but at least it would come regular. I would send it all straight home on account of my father still being poorly. He had been sick for so long now that another of my brothers at age fourteen had to go out to work. He was also sent up to our uncle Dr. Button, married to my mother's sister, in Port Byron to labor in his drug store there. We used to live up there near my mother's family, the Sayres and the Buttons. My mother was a Sayre before she married father and became a Harnden. I was born up there. We moved down to Waverly New York when I was a boy so my father could make his way in a fresh place.

My mother wrote to me of how badly she worried about how hard my younger brothers had to work. She had made herself ill with this, fretting over my condition, and my father being laid so low.

I wrote her directly back to tell her that I used to think I had to work hard but I never knew what fatigue was until I had marched with my knapsack and other accoutrements day after day, my socks saturated with blood from the blisters. Then I was tired, when I would march until I became faint. When we would stop, I'd drop down in the road. Now that is what I would call hard work.

I said, "Mother, you know not one quarter of the hard times I've had. Now if you think we any of us have to work hard, don't let it worry you in the least for compared to soldiering, it will do us good. I'd rather go over my hard times again than hoax you on this." By these words I hoped to give her some peace from her fretting over her husband and her children.

Now that I had a job to do, they moved me out of the ward and into a nice room with some other hospital workers. The dispensary was as I thought, practically just like Doc Everett's place back in Waverly and I fit right in there. Everything was handy and we had water coming in through pipes and running through the store.

Instead of victuals being dealt out to us, only so much for each man, as was the case in the ward, I now sat down at a table with the other clerks, what they called the "pill boys." We even had a table spread like I would have at home. I got all the food I wanted, even bread and butter. There were other tables about for the doctors and other staff. Our surgeons were fine men, everyone but Baxter. Him I did not like and would never forgive him. There were nine or ten of them real doctors there at Campbell.

After I got into the drug store, we cleaned it up and put it in good order. A surgeon come by who had worked all through the other hospitals in Washington and said ours was the neatest dispensary he had seen. So we felt good about that. The man in charge was Hospital Steward George Wood and a finer fellow never lived. He always had a nice smile on his face. The other clerk was a man named John. They were both very good to me.

George Wood was studying medicine before he come for a soldier. He would have graduated into a doctor in eight months if it hadn't been for the war. I decided after a little while in talking to him that I would study medicine in all the spare time I had and George encouraged me to do so. After all, I had witnessed a great many operations, more than a physician in common practice would in twenty-five years. I knew of a great many instances where the surgeons had taken off arms and legs just for practice. I heard the doctors say so themselves but I thought it rough. I thanked God I had not let them take my hand.

Over the next couple of weeks in June, there were exciting times in Washington. Rumor had it that Robert E. Lee was coming our way again to attack the city by way of Baltimore. He was surely going to follow up on his grand triumph at Chancellorsville. The Army of the Potomac shook itself up and got all set to go march into Maryland again to meet Lee.

When the 107th moved out on June 15th from its camp at Stafford Courthouse, it came through the city. I went over to the depot to try to cetch a sight of my friends but I just missed them. I was very disappointed. It was the hottest day I could remember and I feared for them and all the boys, when they started to marching under that fierce sun. A good many of them would be taken down by the sunstroke, I was sure.

So, the poor boys of the battered Potomac Army were bound for another big campaign up in Maryland somewhere. General Lee had sneaked out of Virginia and come along the Shenandoah Valley. Every man in the city who could hold a gun was drafted to defend the capital, in case of attack. All the men from the hospitals who could possibly be spared had got to go. The lucky boys who had gotten their furloughs from the hospital and gone home for thirty days were called back to their regiments, not so lucky for them now. Me, they kept me on, working in the hospital.

Chapter 20   Gettysburg

Before the looming battle, I expected to be called to go back to the regiment at any moment, but it never happened. George Wood said he thought it was on account of blood loss and the camp fever had left me in such a delicate state. He added he judged I was doing a good job where I was. It turned out later he asked the higher-ups to keep me there with him in the dispensary.

It was true that tho my hand was healing well and I had only a scar across my face from the brush at Antietam, my weakness from the fever had returned and dogged me throughout my days. I tired unaccountably and quickly.

News from home in a letter on the June 28th was that Father had recovered his health and there was some talk of him entering the ranks as a surgeon for a New York regiment. I hated to hear of it and wrote to him about the matter straight off.

I said in my letter, "Father, if you wish to contribute to my happiness, you will do so more than in any other way by NOT going into the army! You may think different, but I have seen so much of soldier's life, that I take it upon myself to contradict your thoughts. That is, if they are different from my own. I know your constitution, not as well as you of course, but well enough to know by experience that you cannot stand a soldier's life. You know you cannot stand to ride in the saddle for long. Even if you should go as a surgeon of a regiment and ride instead of march, you could not take it. I would as soon lose an arm as see you go into the service for it seems as tho you were needed at home to take care of your family."

I think my words must of dissuaded my father for there was no more mention of him joining the service after that.

Then we heard that Old Abe had took Joe Hooker off the top spot of the army and replaced him with a corps commander named General Meade. I knew little of the man. I just prayed that he would take better care of our boys and not let so many of them get killed off as Hooker done.

A few days after that, in the beginning of July, news began to trickle into Washington of a terrible battle being played out sixty miles due north of us in Pennsylvania between Meade's boys and Robert E. Lee. The fighting raged for three days around a little spot they called Gettysburg[1]. I prayed day and night for my friends.

Word soon came that after a three day battle of furious intensity, General Lee finally had to admit defeat and pull his boys back. Seemed as though the rebs wouldn't be visiting Washington after all! We had finally whipped them!

Folks said that Lee had a wagon train over ten miles long carrying his casualties back to Virginia and even then some of the reb dead and wounded were left out on the field for our boys to bury or see to. I heard the rebs lost wholly one third of the boys they had brung with them into Pennsylvania. I figured that without Stonewall, Lee couldn't scheme up the kind of daring battle plans he could in the past.

Quick on the heel of the news of the victory at Gettysburg, we got the glorious word that General Grant had finally taken Vicksburg[2]. This time it proved to be true. The city had fell to his siege which meant that control of the whole Mississippi River was now in Union hands. I thought for sure the war would be coming to a close pretty quick and my boys in the regiment would be coming home soon.

But then I learned that General Williams had to take the 12th Corps including the 107th to follow the skedaddling Lee, marching from the battlefield at Gettysburg straight back into Maryland and continuing along without rest for what now amounted to five straight weeks was what I figured.

Down they went once again all the way to Kelly's Ford on the Rappahannock to make sure Lee's army stayed south and didn't try any desperate moves.

The 12th Corps reportedly got picket duty to do along the river. I knew my friends must have been completely wore out by then, though I heard the 107th come through the Gettysburg brush with only one man dead and one wounded. Edgerton wrote to say the heat was so bad along the march to Kelly's they had thrown off all their blankets and extra clothing & such. I never could have stood such marches myself.

Feelings in Washington ran high and wild after the great battle at Gettysburg. One and all hoped that the tide had finally turned. But, the price paid had been almost too terrible.

There started an enormous and ghastly flow of wounded pouring like a torrent into Campbell and all the hospitals thereabouts. We pill boys had not a moment to spare but to tend the afflicted, rebs as well as our own. Gettysburg was turning out to be the biggest battle of the whole war with all the tragedy a man could stand to look at.

The photographs[3] in the papers of the battlefield showed us those dead boys laying poor yank beside poor reb. Printed estimates were that eight thousand men were killed with well over twenty thousand injured from both sides, grievous numbers to be sure.

Now that the Union side might actually have gained the upper hand, the anti war folks, those accursed Copperheads, went to ground, fearing that they would not get the settlement they preferred with the rebs and that their opinions wouldn't hold sway any longer in popularity. If our soldier boys found them out around Washington, they would go along and make their lives a misery, by taking their goods & such things. If the Coppers found fault and protested, well, then the soldiers would go right on in and take everything else they got.

That's how Copperheads were served and I said "Good Riddance!"

But, my brother Ed seemed to have fallen under the influence of our relatives up in Port Byron just as I had feared he might, for he picked a fight with me in our letters. He said he sided with the Coppers now. I thought if folks were so fond of their southern brethren, they ought to go join them!

It seemed powerful cruel to me that all my Copperhead cousins in Port Byron chose to stay home to enjoy the peace that we soldiers were suffering and dying for, and then they criticized us for good measure. Most of my cousins up there were marrying off at a terrible rate which also come hard to me, I can tell you. I should have liked to have the leisure to court and marry a pretty girl.

One day in July while I was walking out in the city, I found a photograph of Brigadier General Knipe, the one I had fought under that terrible night of confusion and death in the woods on the 2nd of May at Chancellorsville. The only way we could see him in the darkness that night was by the flashes of rifle fire. I recognized him and bought the picture, then sent it home to my mother to keep safe for me. That night was a dreadful reality which no one could get any idea of until they were in the battle and afterwards they simply couldn't give any description of it.

Turned out that was the very night the newspapers said Stonewall Jackson was shot up and had his arm amputated. It was generally known by then that his own men had mortally wounded him in a mistake of identity.

General Knipe saved me from being taken prisoner or killed that night. He was as brave a man as I ever saw. I felt that I owed him my life.

In August Tenbrook wrote to me that Edgerton had come down with fever and a bad headache while the regiment lay at Kelly's Ford. He had also written to Will's mother to tell her that he and Wiggins would attend to her son with great care. Will was down prostrate for ten days just like I was so they knew it was Typhoid again come into the regiment. A great many of our boys fell ill. By the time Will recovered, Tenbrook told me our company was down to just twenty-six men in good enough health to fight. He didn't see how the army could be ordered out to another battle seeing as how most of the boys was in such rough shape.

None the less, by September, we soldier boys felt the old familiar rumblings and stirrings that meant the high up generals had plans for us lowly infantry again. Not only that but boys out in the field were being sat down on their own coffins and shot dead for desertion. First time I heard of it happening in the 12th Corps was after Gettysburg. The boys said General Williams sure hated to do it but he had to show everyone the army meant business.

Also in September, I got the worst possible news in a letter from home. My little brother Albert had died from a childhood disease[4] and my grandmother Jane in Port Byron had also passed on about the same time.

I turned to my faith as strongly as I could not be taken down with grief thinking that if I ever made it home, little Allie wouldn't be there to meet me at the station and run out with sister Augustas to grasp my hand and welcome me back. My mother was distraught as any mother would be. Not only had she lost her little Allie and her mother, but she had nearly lost her husband and myself over the last months.

I wrote to her and said, "Mother, you spoke of being afflicted and I think you truly are afflicted just now, but you must bear up under the grief for all is for the best, as you know. As regards his death, we are assured it was for the best and was the will of God. And I am glad he died so happy with a smile on his dear face and you at his side till the last. If he had lived, he would have been subject to the temptations and trials of life that are constantly hovering about one, as in the regiment. Albert is spared all such ordeals." I reminded Mother that little Allie would await us in Heaven as would grandmother Jane.

During those bitter days I also wrote often for solace to my acquaintance Amy Bosworth. Since I had been in the hospital, she and I had begun quite a pleasant correspondence. We had known each other in childhood but then her family had moved away from Waverly down into Pennsylvania. Somehow we had kept up with each other off and on. When she heard I was injured she had begun to write me more often. I in turn had written back and before I knew it, our missives were filled with endearments. I found myself thinking of her as someone very special to me.

Those first dark times in the hospital followed by Albert's death were difficult for me. Amy's letters helped me to bear up through those trials. But, I knew my father did not approve of her folks as they were not such strict Methodists as he judged proper. For the first time, I thought his was too strong an attitude for my liking as regards our religion. I did not therefore let on to my parents of my growing affection for the lovely Miss Amy Bosworth.

There was one bit of good tidings. After all my bad doings with Dr. Baxter, he came along and gave me a recommend in writing that said I was a good man of excellent habits and high moral character. I hoped it would set me up to become a hospital steward if I could not get strong enough to go back to the regiment.

Finally in late September, our boys from the regiment come through the city[5] again for a night. This time I succeeded in intercepting them at the depot. My friends and I spent the night together out spreeing on the town. By that time I was quite accustomed to drink and a good cigar so I was able to keep up with those crazy boys and all their carryings-on. Washington offered every temptation, there being so many soldiers and convalescents there. Of course, the boys teased me a good deal about my being a pill boy. But before we parted in the morning Tenbrook admitted to me he should not have recognized me easily when he first saw me on account of the slightness of my figure and my general pallor.

Wiggins said in a fatherly fashion, "Harnden, I think it best you try to stay out of the regiment for it is a damned terrible business they have us up to mostly and you look to be only a shade of the man you once were," then he puffed out his chest and tried in every way to look the equal to Tenbrook in toughness and dignity.

I stood about on the platform with them until the very last moment when they were loaded into the cars. Most of the men in the brigade were still so drunk from the night spent abroad in the city that it made for a boisterous scene. There was fighting breaking out here and there even on the train. I feared there might be a riot for a great many of the boys were in a state of high anxiety as to where the army was sending them. A good many thought they were bound for Dixie and they sorely wished they didn't have to go.

It seemed to me that morning in Washington that the whole Potomac Army was on the move again. I felt awful sorry for my friends. I knew they had some hard marches and fights ahead.

As I watched the train pull out I said to myself, "and what are we 'hospital bummers' doing about it?"

That was what folks had taken to calling us pill boys and others working in the hospitals, that or "hospital rats." As if we were shirkers and skulkers, pretencing illness to get out of the war. Well, I didn't feel we were doing a great deal but I knew we weren't to blame for it. If I was rugged and could have stood it out at the front, they would have put me there and I would have done my duty if ever I could. But they held me fast in the hospital and I was stuck.

After the boys left, I set to work three times as hard as I ever did at home, even when we worked in the tobacco fields. We dispensed medicine all day long to thousands of patients. Still, I did not count it as anything besides what the boys in the regiment had to endure.

Sometimes I felt so angry on their behalf! Especially when I thought of the hardships of the soldier in the service for three years (unless shot sooner) and then I would think of the Copperheads of the North who stayed home! And many of them could vote in the election whereas so many of us boys were not of age and so had no say in the politics[6] of the matter.

The Coppers were constantly talking, writing in the newspapers, and in every way in their power, working against the Government and calling our soldiers "dogs," when the soldiers were the very ones protecting the Coppers' homes and lives. It made me feel as though I never wished to see one of them snakes alive again on Earth, even though some of them used to be my own good friends and even family members. My feelings for the rebs was love compared to what I felt for the Copperheads of the North. I wished the law was to hang them!

In October, I learnt that General Williams had taken the Division all the way down to Chattanooga[7], Tennessee to join up with a General named Sherman[8] in order to fight the johnnies down there. It seems the army had moved a vast quantity of men down to that region, all by rail. My boys were now far, far away from me. I felt this separation most keenly.

1. The Battle of Gettysburg

On June 28th, 1863, General Joe Hooker and his huge Potomac Army (estimated to be over 100,000 men) were in transit from Washington to Pennsylvania. They were on their way to challenge Robert E. Lee who was leading his Army of Northern Virginia (estimated at under 75,000 men) into Union territory once again. The fiery and arrogant Hooker grew frustrated with another Union commander stationed at the garrison in Harpers Ferry and he handed in his resignation to President Lincoln as an expression of outrage and protest. Lincoln, long tired of Hooker's antics, called his bluff, accepted the resignation, and demoted Hooker back to a Corps commander position.

Though Union armies and navies were at last having some successes in other parts of the country, Lincoln recognized that the matter of the war most likely depended on the outcome of the dispute over the state of Virginia and the capital cities of Richmond and Washington in the Eastern Theater. He was going to have to beat Robert E. Lee very close to home. He no longer believed that the big talking, underperforming Joe Hooker could manage it. So Lincoln called a native Pennsylvanian named General Meade, a veteran commander of the 5th Corps, up from the ranks to lead the Army of the Potomac.

Meade took the reins of the army on June 29th, 1863.

During this period, every able bodied man in and around Washington was armed and called on to either protect the city or rejoin their regiments in the field. Rufus did not know if he would have to go along. Everyone was aware that something big was imminent as Lee was once again getting dangerously close to the North's key cities.

The greatest and most famous battle of the Civil War began just a few days after Meade took command, around a small town in Pennsylvania called Gettysburg. The town was only sixty miles due north of Washington. As June ended, Lee's and Meade's armies moved closer and closer to each other but neither commander actually knew where the other one was headed.

General Lee's 'eyes,' namely a division of about 6,000 cavalry commanded by General Jeb Stuart had left the main Southern army and circled around behind the Union position. Then they got distracted and cut off, so that they were unable to report the results of their scouting missions to Lee until the 2nd day of July, after the battle had started. General Lee on the verge of attacking on June 31st, was as he put it, "going in blind."

General Meade was also going in blind. He only knew that he was on the way to finding General Lee's army whose progress had been shielded from view by the mountains. Neither general had a chance to choose the ground. The battle was joined when a brigade of rebels, sent out to procure much needed supplies from the local populace in Gettysburg, chanced to observe some of Meade's cavalry on a high ridge, just west of the town.

The 107th NY were at the battle of Gettysburg on the days of 1st, 2nd, and 3rd of July. They were still in the 12th Corps, 1st Division,

3rd brigade with Generals Slocum, Williams, and Ruger commanding. Williams was in a better mood about fighting now that Hooker was out and they had General Meade for their new commander. Meade was, in William's estimation, "a gentleman and an officer."

Colonel Nimon Crane, the 107th's Regimental Chaplain, known by then as the 'fighting Parson," was in charge of the regiment. He had only 319 men with him when he went into the field. Diven, back from Elmira, was also along for the ride.

The regiment did its part to repel a series of rebel attacks on the Union positions during the first two days. On the first day, the 1st and 11th Corps were already fighting it out with Lee's men just to the north of the town. Ruger's brigade was sent to the right side of the Union line and tasked with building extensive breastworks which they worked on until nightfall.

July 1st resulted in a Confederate advance with the Union forces driven back but holding onto the series of ridges and high hills outside of town where their cavalry had first been spotted. General Lee, ever more confident and increasingly determined to break the Army of the Potomac once and for all, decided that his men could take the hill positions the next day. He ordered the necessary assaults for the morning. Though the rebels gained some ground again that 2nd day, General Lee was proved wrong. The Union forces received reinforcements and could not be dislodged from their strong positions that lay in a fish hook formation along the high ground.

The 107th NY spent July 2nd marching to reinforce a position at a hill called the the Round Top but then counter marched when it was found that their services were not needed there. However, when they returned to their original position just after dark, they found that Confederates had taken possession of most of their breastworks and were ready to flank attack the rest of the Union army the next day. The Division had to sit tight and wait for daylight to try to roust the rebels.

Will Edgerton wrote to his mother, "In the morning, we was in a pickle, the enemy was in our breastworks and we had to get them out, the best way we could."

General Williams, in command of the first division, realized that a frontal attack would lose him easily half his men. Instead, he positioned several batteries in a flanking position to the rebels and commenced to shell them and their batteries with a terrible hail of fire for two to three straight hours. Then he ordered the shelling stopped and sent in the infantry.

The rebels, Edgerton said, "fought manfully" but could not stand up to the twofold attack. At 3 o'clock they withdrew from the fortified positions and Williams' men reoccupied them successfully. Though the men of the division came under very intense fire from sharpshooters and counterattacks, they were able to hold onto the position throughout the rest of the day without much loss of life.

The battle peaked during the 3rd day of fighting when Lee gambled everything and sent 12,500 men to attack the Union center on the aptly named Cemetery Hill, in a famously risky uphill effort called Pickett's Charge. The ranks of rebel infantrymen and their officers were absolutely decimated by shelling and gunfire from the heights, resulting in very high casualties and an overall Union victory. General Lee was forced to admit defeat, withdraw his troops, and head for the Potomac River and the relative safety of Virginia. It was said that his trains of ambulances and wagons filled with wounded men stretched for 14 miles along the roads behind the retreating army, even though he had to leave another 7,000 casualties behind to be cared for or buried by Union troops and medics.

The 107th NY regiment lost only two men in the battle, one wounded and one dead. None of Rufus's friends were hurt.

Around fifty thousand men from both armies became casualties of one sort or another over the three day period. Lee lost almost a third of the 75,000 men he had come with including many of his officers, and Meade lost about a quarter of his 100,000 men. The total number of men killed was in the neighborhood of eight thousand, the most of any battle of the Civil War.

The day after the Battle of Gettysburg ended, on July 4th, Vicksburg fell to General Grant in the Western theater of the war.

2. General Grant and Vicksburg

Grant's worth as a commander had come under harsh criticism from the Democrats and even members of Lincoln's own Republican party in the past. They attacked Grant for his military failures and his well-publicized struggles with whiskey.

Ironically, Grant's recognition of his drinking problem and his efforts to discipline himself, had transformed him into a humble, thoughtful man, painfully aware of his own shortcomings and vulnerabilities. He was not one to puff himself up like Hooker and so many of the other generals. Lincoln appreciated this quality and loyally defended Grant to his many critics.

Luckily for Lincoln, a determined and grateful General Grant did not give up his relentless efforts in the Western Theater. By April he had developed a well thought out plan to take Vicksburg. It took him until the beginning of July to accomplish his goal but he was ultimately successful. Grant went on to lead the Union to its ultimate victory in 1865, building upon his accomplishments in the West.

3. The Photographs in the Newspapers

The science of photography was an emerging technology that was changing the landscape of war, this time by revealing its horrors in close-up black and white detail to noncombatants at home. Though there was a well established tradition of using excellent illustrators to provide hand drawn pictures for newspapers and publications like Harpers Weekly newspaper, no drawing, however skillfully rendered, could provide the impact and immediacy of a photograph taken on a battlefield.

The technology, still in its infancy, had come from France where the Daguerreotype method was developed in 1825. It had been discovered that if a plate covered in a coat of certain chemicals was exposed to the variegated light emanating from a scene, the material darkened and hardened to form a picture of the subject.

These were the 'plates' that Rufus asked his parents to send to him of his little sister Augustas. They were one of a kind and involved no negatives nor could prints be made from them. The subjects had to sit breathlessly still for several long minutes while the plate was being exposed, hence the formal and often frozen looks on their faces.

During the 1850's photographic science had made a great leap forward. By this time it was also growing in popularity and prestige. There were multiple commercial photographic studios in NYC for instance. One of these was run by Matthew Brady, the most famous of all the Civil War photographers, and the man considered to be the father of modern photojournalism.

Brady persuaded President Lincoln to allow him to take his equipment and assistants right onto a battlefield in 1861 so that he could take pictures during an engagement. This proved to be overly ambitious. Brady lost everything in the chaos of the battle and had to go home and rethink his approach. Using his own money, he was able to organize portable darkroom wagons, each with a two man team. These he began to send onto the battlefields after the fighting was over. He almost never attempted action scenes again. Two men were necessary to take each photograph. An assistant would mix the chemical solution and coat a piece of glass with it, dry it, and finally immerse it in silver nitrate to make it sensitive to light. All this work was done in the confines of the darkened wagon. Then he would rush it out to the photographer who had set up the big boxy camera and focussed it at an unshifting scene or subject. Once in the camera, the plate would be exposed to light for about a minute, then it was rushed back to the wagon to be developed. It was a very difficult process but once accomplished it rendered a glass negative from which multiple prints could be made. Brady's traveling darkrooms began to produce graphic images of the terrible scenes left in the aftermath of the battles. These were printed in newspapers across the country. Many men worked for him and learned their skills at his knee who then broke away from his studio and became Civil War photographers in their own right.

After the war Brady tried to get the US government to pay him for all the work he had done but he was not given much for his five thousand negatives. He eventually got $25,000 when he needed at least $125,000 to recoup his investment. He went bankrupt and died alone and penniless. Nonetheless, his photographs are now in the Library of Congress and belong to all the citizens of the United States.

There were a number of Southerners who took pictures of the war but these photographs were lost. Out of humiliation over their defeat, Southern professionals systematically and bitterly destroyed their plates and negatives after General Lee's surrender in 1865.

The photographs from the battlefields, especially of the dead, put a human face on the war and brought it home every time a civilian opened a newspaper.

In July 1863, the American poet Oliver Wendell Holmes Sr. wrote: "Let him who wishes to know what war is look at this series of illustrations.

These wrecks of manhood thrown together in careless heaps or ranged in ghastly rows for burial were alive but yesterday." The fact that his own son was among the severely wounded at Antietam must have put quite a dent in the heart of the poet for all the young men who were so 'carelessly' thrown away.

4. Childhood Disease

Rufus's youngest brother Albert, age 9, succumbed to what was known as a 'childhood disease.' It was not uncommon for children to die of such illnesses in the 1860's, in fact, 1 in 10 of the young did not make it through their teenage years. Sometimes whole families or all their children were wiped out by a single bout of infectious disease. Again, there was simply no understanding of how to prevent or treat even the simplest of infections. The predominant illnesses that killed off the young were measles, mumps, chicken or small pox, and respiratory infections like influenza, croup, and pneumonia.

Rufus tried to handle the sad news from home as a good Methodist should, with faith that Albert had gone on to a better life with God and would be waiting to welcome them all home when they each passed over into heaven.

5. The Regiment Came Through the City

Little did Rufus or the boys in the regiment realize that the 107th NY was part of the biggest relocation of troops, over the greatest distance, in the least amount of time, that had ever been performed.

New rail technology made possible something that could not have been done even a decade earlier. Leading up to this mass military movement and the need for it, many dramatic events had transpired during the first three weeks of September, 1863 in the Western theater of the war.

After his defeat at Gettysburg, General Lee sent two of his Divisions to Tennessee to help the rebel army there challenge Union forces that had lately captured the very strategically important town of Chattanooga. Lee wanted the city back, and badly.

Once the two Confederate Divisions got to Tennessee, they put the city of Chattanooga under siege. President Lincoln and his war cabinet had to take swift action to deal with the dire situation in the city. So they also sent a portion of their army down to Tennessee. The 11th and 12th Corps, now commanded by General Hooker and consisting of 16,000 men, went from Virginia down to Tennessee by rail. Lincoln then appointed General Ulysses S Grant to take over leadership of all the Union armies in the Western Theater.

Along for the big ride with the rest of the 12th Corps, the 107th NY came back to Washington and then transferred over to the Baltimore & Ohio line which carried them west into Illinois. From there they travelled, still by rail, south to Tennessee, arriving in Nashville in the beginning of October.

6. No Say in the Politics

Rufus, at age 18, was too young to go home to vote, and perhaps it was lucky that he could not get home because his family was going through a bout of grief and turmoil at the time over the two recent deaths, and now his late grandmother's will. It seemed Jane Sayre had owned a half share in a 185 acre farm at the time of her passing and had left instructions that this should be sold and the money given out equally to her four daughters, Harriet, Martha, and their two other sisters, Sarah and Nancy, who had married two brothers, David and Walter, in the Smith family of Port Byron.

But, Jane had also stipulated that before her estate was divided up, Harriet and her husband Dr. Button, also of Port Byron, should be reimbursed for her housing and care for the past three years that she had lived with them, including medicines. Now the family had to go to court to settle Dr. Button's claim on what amounted to a substantial portion of Jane's estate. It seems that during the hearing, he made some disparaging remarks about Harriet's mother's financial situation which upset the daughters, including Martha.

So, there was no peace and quiet back in Waverly for Rufus to enjoy even if he had been able to get there on a furlough. Nor was there any peace to be had between the families over politics. The Harnden's many relations in Port Byron, where Ed was now working in one of the Smith brothers' mercantile stores, were Copperhead sympathizers. Ed was having a good time there with his cousins, most of whom had decided to stay home from the war in support of the peace movement. It was as Rufus said, "a copperhead nest" and Ed's participation continued to eat away at Rufus's relationship with his younger brother.

7. Chattanooga

Chattanooga was a well fortified city on the Tennessee River. It was a location of great importance to the Confederacy because of the railroad lines that converged there in the gap between the mountains, as well as its port on a navigable river, and its factories that produced iron related products. The railway connected it to the North through Nashville, or South to Atlanta, Georgia. It was known as 'The Gateway to the Deep South' for all these reasons.

8. General Sherman

General Grant chose Sherman to lead operations in Tennessee and Georgia for many reasons, including a long and trusting friendship between them.

Sherman, another West Point graduate, had a very mixed and unusual career in the army during the war. Known for being moody, depressive, and headstrong, he suffered a nervous breakdown in late 1861 and had to withdraw from command for many months in order to recover. During this time his condition became well publicized. But General Grant did not give up on his friend, just as Lincoln had not given up on him. Grant recognized that Sherman showed flashes of brilliance as a military strategist.

As Sherman said famously, "He stood by me when I was crazy, and I stood by him when he was drunk."

The two also shared a common philosophy as to how the war could be brought to an end as fast as possible, saving untold lives in the long run. The idea was that you forced the enemy to use up all his resources as soon as possible so that he could no longer support a war effort.

The three goals of what Grant and Sherman called "Total War," were to consume or destroy all the enemy's supplies, wreck any infrastructure that supported the armies, and undermine the spirit of the rebellion in any way possible. Sherman therefore directed his soldiers to travel light and eat off the land. They were to spare none of the citizens' food supply. This enabled his men to move very fast once they started and to leave nothing edible behind them.

Another thing they saw eye to eye on was how best to bring the fight to the enemy on the field of battle.

From observing Stonewall Jackson's brilliant flanking maneuver at Chancellorsville, Grant and Sherman had developed a theory that became known as "Maneuver Warfare."

Instead of going straight at the enemy and hoping to win by superior strength, something called "Attrition Warfare," they saw that a force could be split, with part of it then becoming mobile. The mobile force could then make a turning movement and attack at the enemy's side, at one of his weak places, or at his supply lines. These turns had to be executed quickly and secretly if possible, for the elements of shock and surprise were important to the outcome.

It was an excellent way to gain the advantage over a force that was entrenched in strong defensive positions. In a nutshell it meant that one attacked one's enemy's weaknesses not his strengths. General Grant used it with success at Vicksburg, Jackson at Chancellorsville, and now General Sherman perfected the technique as he pursued the Confederate General Johnston's army into Georgia.

General U.S. Grant

Matthew Brady, Photographer

Photographer's Wagon

General Sherman in Atlanta

Dead Soldier

Dead Soldiers

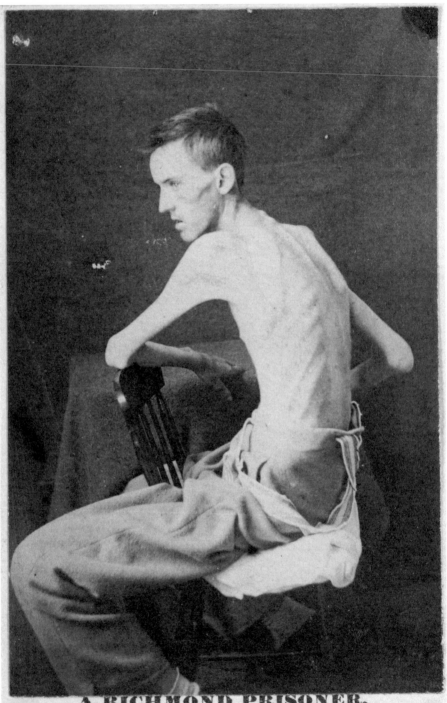

A RICHMOND PRISONER.

*Entered according to Act of Congress, in the year 1864, by
E. Wallace, in the Clerk's Office of the District Court of
the Eastern District of Pennsylvania.*

A Skeleton Boy

Chapter 21   New York Harbor

By the beginning of November, my health had broke down once again from our long days spent in the drugstore, trying to put up medicines for the multitudes of Gettysburg casualties. The doctors then decided to transfer me to another hospital, this time as a patient, for I was weak as a mouse, grown even thinner and paler than ever.

The new place was on a little island[1] in the sound of New York where the air was thankfully very fresh and clean. I hoped I might recover there. It was also a place where a lot of the reb wounded were sent because they couldn't run away, there being only one way off the island, a well guarded ferryboat. It was called DeCamp General Hospital and was by now said to be the biggest hospital in the North. Since Gettysburg it had grown so large.

There were lots of the reb boys recovered enough that they walked about all day and were more prisoners of war than patients. Most of those rebs were friendly to me. They were grateful to be there and not starved to death in some prison camp[2] like the big one up in Elmira. The one the army had built on the same ground next to Foster Pond where we friends had come to the armory to join up. That day seemed an eternity ago though it was only a little over a year and a quarter's time that had passed.

I heard from the rebs that Elmira was a place they all despised to go. They called it "Hellmira." A great many of their boys were dying up there as were many of ours down in the southern hell holes. It seemed the two governments couldn't afford to feed prisoners anything to speak of since they could barely feed us soldiers in the first place. I thought the only way one side or the other would win the thing was to get rid of what little food we had left for the armies. That would stop it for sure.

During those days spent at DeCamp, I was able to go clamming and fishing along the shore. As I regained my strength, I hoped once more that they would give me another job to do in the hospital, so that I could at least do something for the war effort. I felt it was my duty to do all I could.

I found quite a few boys I knew in the pavilions that housed us patients. One of them was Birdsey Hutchins from Waverly. He had fought alongside my old friend Joe Pickering in the 141st NY.

Birdsey was so badly stunned by a shell at Gettysburg that he had lost his voice completely and could not utter a single word since. I brought him along to be my roommate in the same pavilion as me. Since he was not fit for any service in the field, the doctors had put him to writing out paper work and forms & such. I could find nothing wrong about his tongue or throat so I had hopes that he could recover his speech sometime.

Edgerton wrote me one letter from Tennessee and told me life down there went very hard for everyone, even all the citizens of the South. He said the poor white trash were the lowest kind of folk. Half starved and uneducated and if anyone had any doubts about the damning effects of slavery on all but the richest class, well they had better come down and see for themselves. The rich families had fled out of the countryside and left the poor folks to famine and death. He said we should grieve and fight for the poor whites as well as for the negro.

After a month or so, surprise, surprise! Dr. Baxter wrote another letter to the hospital explaining what a good druggist I had proved to be back at Campbell.

It said:

To whom it may concern; This is to certify that Corp R S Harnden 107th N Y was on duty as clerk in the Dispensary of the Hospital and proved himself a man of strict integrity and sobriety.

We the undersigned take pleasure in recommending him as an industrious, faithful, and competent man in the discharge of the duties assigned him while here."

It was signed by Baxter and my old boss, George Wood.

The next day almost, they had me back dispensing medicine and they moved me and Birdsey into the steward's mess where we lived as well as I could ask.

I was in my new room one day when the surgeon in charge gave me orders to report to Head Quarters immediately. I done so not knowing but I was going into the guard house or something of that kind. But instead I was accompanied into the Dispensary by the Chief Steward who politely saluted the Steward in charge and told him he was relieved from duty and must forthwith turn the Dispensary over to me. He stepped out and I directly in as head man. Imagine that! I said to myself, very surprised.

Then I had a fellow to do all the work, build fires, wash bottles, & such things. I just put up prescriptions and run the machine all to myself. They had another shop where they compounded the tinctures, syrups, and liquors. I could order it all and they would send it to me by the quantity. There were only nine hundred patients in the hospital at that time, in some eighteen pavilions with one surgeon for each pavilion.

I found it much easier to resist temptations on the island than back at Campbell so I was living right. Washington was a city full of temptations. I didn't think there was a city of Washington's size in all the world where there was so much wickedness. I had seen hundreds of soldiers completely ruint in the haunts of vice of which that city abounded. It taught me a lesson though, one to last me a lifetime.

But the main reason I had now quit smoking was because my Miss Amy induced me to stop by way of her letters. She would also not have me drinking any beer or porter.

I tried to keep up my correspondence with my brother Ed but he wrote to me that he was a Copperhead now!

I told him back that if it were so then he was no more my brother, and I meant it too. I would have disowned my own father if he were a Copperhead and despised a soldier. Thank Heaven Father did not. On the contrary he loved the soldiers. After that, I wrote to Ed several times but received no reply for a long while.

I worked at the hospital on David's Island through the long bleak winter and into the spring of 64, never knowing if I was to be called up for a soldier. I heard not one word from the boys down in Tennessee[3]. It worried me a good deal and I hoped that they were settled somewhere for the winter months uncalled upon to march or fight.

In January, we got a new head man from Fort Schuyler Hospital named Dr. Webster, as well as his whole department. He come along with quite a story to tell us of what had occurred at his last place, concerning a boy who was a patient of his there.

It seemed the poor boy had been badly wounded at Fredericksburg, a terrible injury to the chest and right upper arm. He was hospitalized in Washington for a good deal of time and came through with a useless arm. The boy was terrified that he would be sent back to his regiment so he ran away from the hospital as many are want to do in their desperation. Five months later, still feeling the effects of his wound, if anything worse than before as it had festered, he turned himself in at Dr. Webster's hospital.

Dr. Webster operated on the boy's arm in an effort to make it heal properly. But the army come along and decided they wanted to arrest the boy and take him away as prisoner for desertion. The good Doctor said 'no way,' that the boy had an open surgical site in his chest for one thing. He wouldn't give the boy up so the army court marshaled the Doc for his troubles. They then sent Doc Webster on to us which was our luck for he was a very good head man and did excellent things for DeCamp.

He said he had no idea if his relocation was punishment or advancement by the army in this strange affair.

Once he came to us along with all his other staff, we had twenty-five doctors and more people to help us do our work, which was a blessing. Before, I had caught at least three doctors who were so completely tired out they made bad mistakes, where if I had put up the medicine as they prescribed, the patient would have died in twenty minutes.

I said, "No sirree! It is too large a dose," and I would not do it.

Then during my early spring months at DeCamp, General Grant got a whole bunch of prisoners back from the rebs in a swap for some of theirs. It was called a 'prisoner of war exchange' and it was a terrible thing to behold.

At our hospital, we received hundreds of these poor souls, many having chronic diarrhea and were the worst looking I ever saw. About one hundred I judged didn't average eighty pounds of flesh on them. They were perfect living skeletons[4]. They came from a prison in Charleston. Five or six of them died as soon as they were taken off the steamer and I didn't think a fourth of the ones we had would get well.

Then we had to put up medicines wholesale, more than a drugstore at home would put up in a month, every single day. I got so tired during those times I could hardly stand up.

But by the time I turned nineteen in February of 64, my own health was getting good again and I was contented in spite of the hard work. I kept at it, trying to get taken on as a steward with better pay but it never amounted to anything.

After my birthday I got a letter with the news that Edwin had fell sick enough that he had to come back home to Waverly so my mother could nurse him. I wrote to her and suggested that when he recovered, they send him down to me so he could do hospital work. I was in need for another man in the dispensary and it might as well be Ed. He would have to sign a citizen's contract

for a year and would get paid the same as me, as well as room
and board. I figured it would be good for him and cure him of his
cousins' unpatriotic views.

I still did not get even a note from my friends in Tennessee, but
now and then one of the other boys from the 107th would come
back through New York City wounded or sick. I would go over
to see them if I could and try to cetch up. I heard from them the
regiment was strung out guarding the railroad from Nashville to
Chattanooga all winter long against guerrilla raiders.

In the beginning of March, the same old thing started up,
namely, the army getting ready for another big round of battles
and actions & such. Springtime to me now meant green leaves
on the trees and a fresh crop of torn bodies in the fields. Old
Abe called on General Grant and put him in charge of all the Union
military forces there were anywhere and everywhere because that
man had showed he could WIN!

I guess the story was that General Grant had been down in
Chattanooga, getting us out of the big fix[5] we were in down there.
He returned to Washington after his promotion to top man and
left General Sherman, his best friend and confidante, so they said,
in charge down in Tennessee. As near as I could make out the
107th was still with General Williams down there.

I thought I might be called up along with everyone else but tho
I was stronger than before, the fragility of my health prevented it
once again. Then Ed arrived on the island right side up and we set
him to work in the drug store at once. I could not tell if he liked
it but we got along all right and even began to have some good
times together, our Copperhead fuss forgotten.

Then I developed a terrible headache soon after he got there and
much to my surprise, the doctors finally gave me my own furlough.
I went home in April and stayed about two weeks. During that
time Ed wrote to me a friendly letter and teased me considerably

about Amy for I had let him in on my little secret before I left the Island. He asked me if I was "enjoying the society of the lovely, the beautiful, the angelic Miss...well you know who, so I will not trust the precious secret to the uncertainties of the mail."

Amy came over visiting from her home in Pennsylvania and I did greatly enjoy her delightful company although we took pains to conceal the fact of our growing attachment. I was certain my father was not going to be pleased about it. During my stay in Waverly, I finally was able to read some letters from my friends, like ones that Mary had got from Wiggins. It turned out that the mails rarely got through from Tennessee on account of the terrible rebel raiding parties that so bedeviled the railroads down there.

I learnt that the 107th and the good old 12th Corps, along with the 11th Corps, had been rolled into one big new Corps called the 20th under our old friend the famous fighting Joe Hooker. At least the boys said he was not drinking and carrying on like he used to. They were still in one of General Williams' brigades which made me feel better as he was proven to be such a fair man to his troops.

The army down in Tennessee was said to be fixing to march into Georgia led by General Sherman. I supposed they would be chasing the southern part of the rebel army. Up north General Grant was going to cross the Potomac and go after Lee's army again and try for Richmond. I had no doubt that we would settle this thing pretty soon. As usual I was proved wrong as I had been so many times before.

1. A Little Island in the Sound

In the beginning of November of 1863, Rufus, in very poor health, was transferred to another military hospital as a patient. This one was on a small island composed of just 78 acres called David's Island in New York's Long Island Sound.

The hospital grounds were accessible to the mainland only by ferry. The choice of the island for a hospital was due to the high desertion rate among recovering soldiers which had grown to well above 16%. First leased by the government in 1862 as a location for a new hospital, the facility was greatly expanded after the Battle of Gettysburg, most notably by the addition of facilities in which to care for the many Confederate casualties who had been left behind on the battlefield.

It was called De Camp General Hospital and by 1863 was the biggest of all the Union hospitals, housing at one time thousands of patients in hastily erected long wooden buildings and tents on platforms.

As the Confederate casualties recovered, they became captives and the island turned into as much a prison camp as hospital. A wounded rebel would have thanked his lucky stars to have ended up there instead of starving and freezing in one of the other prison camps in the North. On David's Island, with its secured ferry and wide natural moat of cold harbor water, all the patients, staff, and prisoners roamed free if their health permitted it. They were able to garden, clam, and even go fishing to provide themselves with better than the usual army or prison fare.

2. Prisoner of War Camps

The situation surrounding POWs was complicated and had been since the outbreak of the Civil War. At the beginning in 1861, neither side had military prisons that could handle large numbers of enemy soldiers, nor did they have supplies and food for their support. Yet, if captive soldiers were released too soon, they would likely be back fighting for their side again in just a few days or weeks.

In spite of that, the two sides released each others' captives fairly quickly in the first year of war. It was simply not physically possible to hold on to them for any length of time.

Early in 1862, as the war progressed and more and more prisoners were taken into custody, a pact called the Dix-Hill Cartel was developed by the two militaries to handle prisoner exchanges.

Batches of men were organized and swapped in what amounted to a flesh and blood game of cards. Officers were worth several enlisted men, depending on rank, and so on.

This system helped prevent large numbers of prisoners from being detained and accumulating on either side until 1863, when, after The Emancipation Proclamation, the North began to accept black men to serve as soldiers in the US army. Southerners, outraged and ever fearful of any inspiration for their slaves to rebel, refused to acknowledge the black soldiers as prisoners of war if they were caught. They were called 'rebel slaves' and were not afforded any of the previously agreed upon treatment of POWs.

As bad as regular prisoners might have it, blacks soldiers and their white officers had it much worse if they were caught by rebel forces. In fact, their white officers could be shot and the black infantrymen sent into slavery, tortured, or even massacred. While the North struggled with this new snag in the terms of exchange, the swaps slowed down to a crawl, and the numbers of prisoners began to rise as the big battles of 1863 and '64 produced large numbers of captives. Soon places like the armory at Elmira had to be turned into POW camps to house the burgeoning ranks of captives that overflowed other meager facilities. Similar camps were hastily established in the South, often outdoors next to old civilian prisons or forts. The severe lack of resources and infrastructure on both sides meant that these new camps were terribly crude; sometimes just a stockade fence was erected around a dirt yard with no shade or shelter provided for inmates. In Elmira, the horrible conditions the prisoners had to endure were magnified by a high dose of humiliation. The authorities in charge of the prison built viewing platforms above the stockade fence that surrounded the old armory buildings and grounds, where townsfolk and others curiosity seekers could come and observe the men below in their filth and misery.

Starvation, exposure, disease, and lastly hopelessness killed over a quarter of those in the prisons, in places whose names went down in the public record of man's inhumanity to man, places like Andersonville in Georgia, Libby Prison in Richmond, Virginia, and Elmira in New York.

3. The 107th NY During the Winter Months of 1863

The coming of winter in 1863 brought relative quiet to the many fronts of the Civil War. It would remain so until February of 1864 when the spring campaigns kicked into gear.

General Williams and the boys in the 107th NY Regiment transitioned from fighters to a new life as occupiers in foreign territory while they guarded the railway in Tennessee. For the first time, they began to interact with the local people and observe the customs and conditions of Southerners. And they began to write to their loved ones at home about what they saw.

They were not always kind in their assessments, most especially of the poor whites. Nor were the Southerners very kind to them. Though most Southerners stated to their occupiers that they were Northern sympathizers, in fact, they were usually lying.

At Christmas some of the boys of the 107th NY bought several cooked turkeys off of a local vendor for their holiday meal. He had added a nasty ingredient to the recipe and all who partook of the Christmas feast became terribly ill, poisoned in fact. They recovered but their goodwill toward the local populace was seriously eroded.

General Williams wrote to his daughter during their period guarding the railroad describing his location and the locals, as well as his belief as to why social conditions were as bad as they were in the South.

"All the towns along this railroad excepting Murfreesboro are the veriest pretenses, most of them sounding names and nothing else, and the people - the "poor white trash" - are disgusting: the mere scum of humanity, poor, half starved, ignorant, stupid, and treacherous. The women all "dip" snuff: that is, rub their teeth and gums with a pointed stick dipped in Scotch snuff! If anybody doubts the damning effects of slave labor upon the poor whites, let him come into Kentucky and Tennessee and see the poorer classes of whites. Of course, there is a rich and educated class, but they are mostly gone and the poor now stand out in bold relief, with not even a bright background."

He added, " they are vastly inferior to the Negro in common sense, shrewdness, and observation, and in the comforts of life," and that he thought people should feel for the poor Southern white man as well as for the Southern negro.

Edgerton also wrote home about his time in Tennessee. "I was very much deceived in the country here, in stead of being a nice country as I supposed it was, it is a country that I would not live in for the best part, that I have seen, in the first place the inhabitants are about 100 years behind in knowledge and civilization. They don't hardly know what a stove is, they principally use fireplaces in chimneys on the outside of the houses. In the second place the country is almost entirely deserted, the farms are all grown up to weeds and underbrush, the hogs and other animals are hunted down and killed."

"The citizens around here are not but traveling on horseback... often 2 or 3 on together. They don't any of them ride in wagons. It looks rather odd, then they all use the queerest phrases and big words that I ever heard of, most of the ladies use tobacco and all of the men."

Edgerton added, " I have a chance to see slavery in Tenn, it looks horrible. I have seen men nearly not quite as white as I am, that was slaves...I am and always was an Abolitionist and I pray I am on the right side."

4. Skeleton Boys

During the early part of 1864, some final exchanges of the sickest men from the prisons took place and these caused an uproar, particularly in the North. The men that were sent back had obviously been starved and neglected to the point of death. The Northern press published graphic pictures of these poor emaciated soldiers and civilian sentiment was aroused. They became known as "our skeleton boys."

There was plenty of blame to go around for their condition as well as a good deal of hypocrisy and denial as to the treatment of prisoners of war in the Northern camps. Since the breakdown of exchanges had occurred specifically around the issue of black troops and their treatment, Lincoln and the abolitionists were held politically responsible for the failure of the terms of the pact, so much so that Lincoln feared the repercussions would affect his chance of re-election.

Nonetheless, Lincoln and Grant officially put an end to the Dix-Hill arrangement in April of 64, stating that no exchanges would take place until the South agreed to equal rights and protections for black prisoners. It was not until January of 1865 that the CSA finally broke down and accepted the new terms; exchanges resumed at that point but too late for the thousands who had already perished as prisoners of war. Of all the war dead, almost 10% died in the prisons. The numbers of men taken captive during the war were staggering. 144,000 Union men were held in the South, and 215,000 Rebels in the North over its duration. Roughly 30,000 Union and 26,000 rebel men died in captivity, most of them during the last 2 years of the war.

General Grant was especially adamant that all prisoners, black or white, be treated equally, considering it his duty as a commander to protect every one of his soldiers, but he also had other reasons to discontinue the exchanges that had terrible consequences for all the Civil War prisoners. He knew that if he kept every rebel POW out of play he could exacerbate the problem the South was having filling the ranks of its rapidly dwindling armies. The CSA was literally running out of manpower and Grant meant to hurry up the process and end the war as quickly as possible.

He also knew that the stress of having to support thousands of Union POWs in the South was adding to the crushing financial burdens the Confederacy was already facing. Any way Grant could find to drain the South of its remaining resources, he meant to pursue, however brutal it might appear in the short run. Unfortunately, it inevitably followed that prison conditions plummeted to new lows, especially in the South.

In January of 64, in one of those final exchanges to take place before Grant's decree, hundreds of very sick men were shipped North to David's Island from Charleston, NC. In Charleston, they had been kept inside an open stockade in front of the city jail. Most of them were dying of dysentery. Their condition was very shocking to Rufus. It was a ghastly side of the war that he had not seen before. Now, he and the other staff at DeCamp were struggling to keep this large band of unfortunate skeleton boys alive.

5. Chattanooga

A Union General named Rosecrans, in command of The Army of The Cumberland in Tennessee, had determined to drive the rebels out of Chattanooga which he accomplished by early September, 1863.

But the Confederate generals and Jefferson Davis would not let go of Chattanooga so easily; they were determined to reoccupy the city. General Lee packed up his tenacious bulldog of a general, Longstreet, and his entire Corps and sent them all down to Tennessee to capture Chattanooga.

Under the command of Generals Bragg and now Longstreet, the rebel Army of the Tennessee lured General Rosencrans out of the city and cruelly whipped him in a terribly bloody battle at a small nearby town called Chickamauga. Rosencrans lost 30% of his men, almost 2,000, in close combat among the trees and rocky hills by the Chickamauga Creek. But when one of his generals, General Thomas, made a heroic stand to provide cover for the rest of the routed Union Army, Rosencrans was able to withdraw back into Chattanooga and barricade his men in the town.

General Bragg's troops followed and occupied the surrounding mountain heights and ridges that looked down on the city. Then they tore up the big railroad bridge that crossed the Tennessee River at Bridgeport, and utterly destroyed Rosecrans' supply trains, leaving the rocky 55 mile route through the mountains strewn with 800 burned out wagons and literally thousands of slaughtered mules.

Rebel cavalry raiders were even sent to attack the rail line from Bridgeport up to Nashville. Since there was now no way to get food and supplies through to the men in the town, and Confederate spies informed Bragg that the Union men only had six days of rations with them and very little food for their surviving mules and horses, General Bragg wisely chose to sit tight and begin a brutal siege of the town. His men were short of ammunition and he did not think they could prevail in a head to head engagement against an enemy behind dug-in fortifications. But if bullets weren't available, the threat of death by starvation would become quickly all too real for the Union army locked inside the town.

General Rosecrans was so shocked by this humiliating defeat and his army's discouraging situation that he seemed to have lost all will to fight. Within days, his men grew short of rations and their animals began to die. The struggle to survive would last for five terrible weeks, with men reduced to digging kernels of grain out of the dirt in the roads.

On October 23rd, General Grant arrived in the vicinity of Chattanooga to deal with the situation. Within a week, he had managed to open a new and much shorter route through to the Union army under siege, daringly using the Tennessee River instead of the old overland road. This new route was called the Cracker Line. At first, the priority was to get food into the city. After that, blankets, fuel, and clothing to counteract the coming of colder fall weather, then lastly, Grant began to build up supplies of munitions within the city in preparation for a battle to end the blockade.

Grant started his move to break the siege of Chattanooga in November. Over a period of three days, his men mounted a series of carefully planned attacks and successfully broke the rebel lines that held the area outside the city. General Bragg was forced to withdraw and move off toward Georgia, leaving the whole state of Tennessee to be occupied by the Union army. One of the attacks that broke the siege was made by General Hooker and three divisions against the rebel forces that were entrenched on Lookout Mountain.

The mountain rose 1200 feet above the valley where Chattanooga lay along the winding river. On three sides it was nothing but cliff and rock. Access lay on the fourth side by way of a ridge. As long as rebels held the lofty position on the mountain, there could be no safety in the city below.

A unique and unusual weather pattern characterized the mountain wherein a layer of fog formed during the day and then sank to hover halfway down its slopes, obscuring the land and the river beneath it. Most of the battle was fought on the ridge and sides of the mountain but some occurred on the heights above the fog and so it came to be called 'The Battle Above the Clouds.' Hooker's men were spoiling for revenge for the awful Union casualties suffered so recently at Chickamauga. They went into the fight yelling, "Remember Chickamauga!" and got what they were after in blood payment.

Lookout Mountain became famous and even revered in the romanticized mythology of the Civil War as a particularly dramatic location. In the coming year, the US Army would need to build hospitals in the South to treat the constant flow of wounded men generated by the campaign. Lookout Mountain was chosen as a safe and secure site for a new facility. Rufus would come to know its grounds, its mists, and its beautiful views of the countryside below very well.

Exchange Prisoners by William Waud

Battle of Lookout Mountain by Kurz and Allison

1. Head Quarters.
2. Rebel Camp.
3. Hospital.
4. Cook House.
5. Death House.
6. Death Line.
7. The Island.
8. Sutler's Camp.
9. Police Quarters.

ANDERSONVILLE PRISON
AS SEEN BY
JOHN L. RANSOM,
AUTHOR AND PUBLISHER OF "ANDERSONVILLE DIARY, ESCAPE AND LIST OF THE DEAD."
WASHINGTON, D. C.

10. Hospitals along the Death Line.
11. Market Street.
12. Broad Street.
13. Inside Stockade.
14. Second Line Stockade.
15. Third Line Stockade.
16. Lieut. Head Quarters.
17. Washing Place.
18. Rifle Pits.
19. Aster House Mess.

Andersonville Prison

Elmira Prison

Chapter 22   Tennessee

When I returned to the hospital on David's Island after my furlough, I barely had time to speak to my brother Edwin before I got hit with the news that I was being called back to the regiment. I was bound for a soldier boy again! At last I would be reunited with my friends and be part of the brave action at the front!

The army began by sweeping up a whole bunch of us recovered convalescents. We were then sent over to another much smaller island[1] in the harbor called Bedloes. From there we would go on to Tennessee to join our regiments.

After several long and lonely days spent walking about the little island and gazing across the water toward the bustling city of New York, we traveled on to Ohio by train. It wasn't much of a pleasant journey as there were some skulks aboard who took every chance they got to try to skedaddle. The officers posted guards along the cars so we were all obliged to be such under a close guard that we couldn't leave the cars for any purpose.

Once we got to the city of Cincinnati, we were put into a one room barracks, sixty men in all and the way they carried on wasn't slow. The guards had to keep order and prevent the building from being demolished which was undertaken by skulks at one point but prevented. All the boys loudly denounced Cincinnati as a Copperhead hole and our place of the one guarded room there equal to Libby prison in Richmond.

We were not allowed out of the room on no conditions. Eat, drink, sleep, wash, and further some smoked, chewed, spit, swore, and threw hard tacks, all in one room with a small side room attached where we could defecate. It grew rather smudgy and made it difficult to breath freely. I couldn't stand it in such a place for long. I was in hopes that we would leave for Nashville within the week.

Thankfully, after a few days we boarded a steamer named the General Buel U S Mail and started for Kentucky. The steamer was one of the finest and largest of the river steamers and made the 150 mile run from Cincinnati to Louisville.

I took a position on top of the boat where I enjoyed the fine and refreshing breeze and the beautiful scenery along the banks of the river. The trees were beginning to leaf out and the grass and grain looked fresh and green. The fruit trees were all in blossom too, giving forth the most fragrant perfume. I found everything was in a high state of cultivation, at least one month in advance of New York State. The people had their gardens made, their fields plowed, and everything moving off as tho a terrible war was not in evidence. It was the most inviting scenery I had ever seen. Especially for a soldier.

To add to the scenery along the river, we had the pleasure of seeing a great many people, especially young ladies who thronged the banks of the Ohio as the Old U S Mail hove in sight. The girls of Indiana were, I thought, the finest, for every wave of the handkerchief you could get a response.

When we got to Louisville, they put us up in another sort of barracks or rendezvous for soldiers going to the army. It was again a hard place. Luckily, I found a little squad to bunk with who were all cheerful fellows. We chose to feel fine over our trip and to enjoy it hugely instead of whine. But there were some of the other boys were down in the mouth and they felt, "I don't want to go to Dixie and this is awful hard & such."

I was therefore in very high hopes of going on to Nashville soon by rail. I was anxious to get to the regiment for it was far more preferable than being twisted about on the way, and not having the opportunity of seeing the country as you would if you were a free man.

When I looked out on the civilians enjoying themselves and having every luxury and everything they could wish for, while we who were sacrificing health and life for them were looked upon by the larger share of them as mere animals and not men. It was poor encouragement. That is what made one half of the men in the army so reckless. It made us ready to come home and fight those who weren't our friends, didn't respect us, and didn't make allowances for some of our rude actions which were on account of the circumstances we were in.

When I began to think of these things, I had to check myself and say I didn't sacrifice these things of my own accord. Though I grumbled about it and felt our lot to be ever so hard, I tried not to dwell upon it.

Since we had left New York, our bill of fare extended to a morning piece of pork and some hard tack. At noon, not feeling a very craving appetite for hardtack we would partake of nothing. For supper hard tack and pork. Only somedays a little coffee which we considered the very staff of life to a soldier. I wasn't used to it and lost weight again.

We heard many tales of hardship and tragedy along our way. One day we learnt of a train going to Nashville from Louisville, a distance of three hundred miles or more, which met a train coming up and they stepped into each other in a very unfriendly manner. The engines were entirely demolished and eighty men wounded, three killed, all from the 10th Indiana Cavalry. I knew nothing of the poor horses but I could imagine they were many of them sorely injured.

When we got to Nashville, we stayed in a building called the Zollicoffer House[2], named after a general of the rebel army who had taken some terrible foolish missteps in his campaign and got himself and many others killed. Some said the place was meant for a fine hotel but the war had swallowed it up for soldiers, first theirs, now ours. It was a large building, one of the largest I have ever seen, built up five stories of brick and rumored to hold 365 rooms. It was very rough, not being finished, and I was glad to get out of there quick for I didn't like the feel of the place. I heard later it was thought to be haunted by a murdered bride or some such.

In looking about the countryside during my travels through the South, I found it to lack enterprise compared to the North. Most of it looked like a wilderness.

Now and then we passed a plantation where the negro did all the work while the white man stood by, a lazy indolent fellow. Over the whole way, I only saw three or four white men at work and they were near a house or barn, not out in the fields where the labor was hot and hard. In all that way, I didn't see but one schoolhouse. Of course, there were high schools in the cities but the poor couldn't attend.

I thought that if yankee ingenuity, education, and enterprise were introduced into the country around there, it would far surpass the North, for it possessed advantages the North did not. Its rivers were great and it had other sources to make for mercantile advantages.

Our trip from Nashville was a tough one for the road was infested with the infamous General Forrest's guerillas[3]. We were crowded into freight cars and expected the whole ways to be run off the track or come under attack from his devils. The railroad wound its way over the stoney summits and through dark ravines, valleys, and around the biggest rockiest mountains I ever beheld. The railroad was a purely military one and like these military cities, was pretty rough. Every mile you could see cars laying beside the track, smashed up, some burned by guerrillas and others destroyed by accident.

1. Bedloe's Island

Tiny Bedloe's Island, further down the coast in New York Harbor was Rufus's first stop on his journey down to Dixie. It was home to a fort and a military hospital.

The island's inhabitants and Rufus had no way of knowing that the ground they wandered was to be famous to an unimaginable degree within a few decades.

In 1865, at a dinner party celebrating the end of the Civil War, the chairman of the French Anti-Slavery Society proposed that the French people give the United States a gift of an enormous bronze statue, a work of art in honor of Liberation and the end of slavery. Twenty years later, The Statue of Liberty was erected on Bedloe's Island. In 1956 the island was renamed Liberty Island, and its previous name faded from memory.

2. The Zollicoffer House

The enormous brick building that Rufus described was called the 'Zollicoffer Barracks' during the war. Before that it had been known as the 'Maxwell House,' or sometimes 'Orton's Folly' among the citizens of Nashville.

Maxwell House was originally intended to be a grand hotel and would eventually achieve this destiny later on after the dust of war had settled. An ambitious citizen of Nashville, Colonel John Overton, began to build it in 1859, in honor of his wife, Harriet Maxwell, using slave labor. It was a square brick building, five stories tall, encompassing 240 rooms, not quite as many as Rufus had been told. But it was a ridiculous size for a small city of only 16,000 residents, hence its 'folly' nickname.

Only partially finished and running way over budget, the building was taken over by the Confederacy at the beginning of the war to house its soldiers.

Soon thereafter, it was the scene of a horrible accident when several hundred men tried to rush down a wooden staircase at the same time and caused the stairs to collapse. Not many died but survivors sustained crushing injuries, maiming them for life. Also, rumor held that a double murderer fell to his death in the collapse, having just dispatched his own brother and mistress in a love triangle dispute somewhere on an upper floor of the hotel. The huge house with its miles of corridors and warrens of rooms was thought to be haunted after that incident.

When Union troops arrived to occupy Nashville in 1863, they used the building both as a barracks and a military prison. After the war, it was given back to Colonel Overton who resumed construction.

In 1867 the Ku Klux Klan (from the Greek 'kuklos' meaning circle) was officially born in a meeting room at the hotel. The building was finally finished in 1869 and opened at last as an opulent hotel; it became the central gathering place for Nashville's cultural elite for the rest of that century and well into the next.

Seven US presidents and a long list of celebrities stayed there. When President Theodore Roosevelt visited, he enjoyed the coffee served in its fancy dining room so well that he proclaimed it "Good to the last drop," when he finished his cup. The hotel began to package and sell its coffee blend under the brand name 'Maxwell House Coffee' using the presidential quip as its tagline. The venture was a great commercial success story, one that outlived the hotel by many decades.

In the end, the building with a complicated past, and an unknown number of ghosts, burned down on Christmas night in 1961.

The man it was named for during the war, Felix Zollicoffer, had a famous folly of his own. He was a rebel general who, in the Battle of Fishing Creek in 1861, had positioned his troops on the wrong side of a river, putting them directly in the path of an overwhelmingly superior enemy force. When he realized the extent of his mistake, he compounded it by ordering a surprise attack at dawn. The attack failed spectacularly. Though most of his men were able to escape, Zollicoffer made even a third awful mistake when he mistook Union troops for his own men and rode up to speak to them. They shot him full of holes and he died soon afterwards. The episode was known affectionately as 'Zolly's Folly,' and the barracks in Nashville given his name for the duration of the war.

3. Forrest's Guerillas

As part of the rebel rear guard, General Forrest's Cavalry Raiders did everything they could to disrupt the Union's progress as it drove into Southern territory. They destroyed railway tracks, attacked trains, and cut supply and communication lines in a constant barrage of lightning fast strikes, inspiring General Sherman to refer to their leader as 'that Devil Forrest.'

Forrest himself was one of the most remarkable officers to emerge from either side during the war. Dramatic, brilliant, and charismatic, he began life as the son of a poor blacksmith in rural North Carolina. He took the lead of his large and dependent family at the age of 17 due to his father's death.

Without the benefit of any formal education, he managed to procure enough expertise to put his considerable ambition to work as a speculator in many commodities. Real estate, slaves, horses, and agricultural products seemed to turn to gold in his hands.

At the outbreak of hostilities between North and South, he was 40 years old and had amassed a private fortune of one and a half million dollars, making him one of the richest men in the South. He owned plantations and was therefore exempt from service in the army, yet he enlisted. Not only that, he sought no special consideration and enlisted as a private, an unthinkably humble choice for a man of large property and high standing.

As the war progressed, he rose quickly through the ranks, based on his prowess, his horsemanship, and his gift for tactical strategy. When given the command of a large cavalry but no equipment or horses for them, he furnished everything his men needed out of his own pocket. Though he seems to have been a stalwart racist, some of his own slaves served loyally in his cavalry as expert horsemen and fighters, having been carefully trained by their master.

Imposing at a height of 6'2" which put him well above the height of most men of the time, he was athletic, tough, and an accomplished swordsman, said to sharpen his saber blade on both sides for maximum effect. During his 4 years of service in the war, he was wounded several times, once by a minie ball fired straight into his spine. He also had 29 horses shot out from under him and came under fire 179 times. Forrest claimed that his men had taken 31,000 Union men prisoner and that he had killed 33 by his own hand.

All of this made him stand out as a man of exceptional ability, but his real genius was his deep grasp of how best to win a fight. He introduced notions of extreme mobility combined with overwhelming force. When asked the secret to his many successes, he is rumored to have answered, 'Get there first with the most men."

General Grant often remarked that Forrest was the only rebel cavalry officer who scared him.

Known by the nickname 'The Wizard of the Saddle,' Forrest was like a hornet and his cavalry a swarm that plagued and harassed the advancing Union army in Tennessee to great effect. Not a day went by where trains were not derailed or sent crashing into each other, supply depots overrun, and threats made.

To further deepen and mystify Forrest's character, there was a darkness inherent to his war- making. He was known to state that war was quite simply for the purpose of killing men. After the war, he was accused of war crimes. He and his cavalry had apparently been involved in a massacre of hundreds of black and white prisoners in Tennessee, a rumor that Rufus referred to.

After the war, in 1867, Forrest became an early member of the newly formed Ku Klux Klan, signing up at the Maxwell House Hotel in Nashville, room #10. He was sworn in to what he described as a 'protective political military organization.' The initial goals of the Klan were to persuade Blacks not to vote and to return peacefully and willfully to their servitude so that the South could recover both its culture and economy. When these goals proved unfulfillable politically, Forrest led a series of fiery midnight Klan raids to make the point more forcibly.

Eventually Forrest seems to have parted ways with the Klan and grown increasingly uncomfortable with the escalating violence of their activities. By the end of his life, he was supporting reconciliation between the races.

In the years following the war and reconstruction, deprived of his slaves, Forrest lost his Midas touch and although he tried to invest wisely, he ultimately lost everything and died a poor man, living in Memphis in a log cabin salvaged from one of his abandoned plantations. He was buried there in a park that bears his name, as do many establishments throughout the South to this day.

Statue of Liberty, Bedloes island

THE PORT OF NEW YORK.

The Port of New York

General Nathan Forrest, the Cavalry Raider

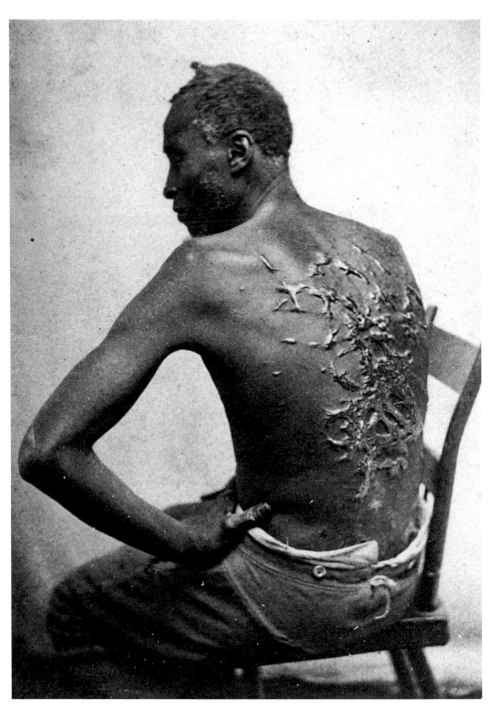

A Slave's Scars

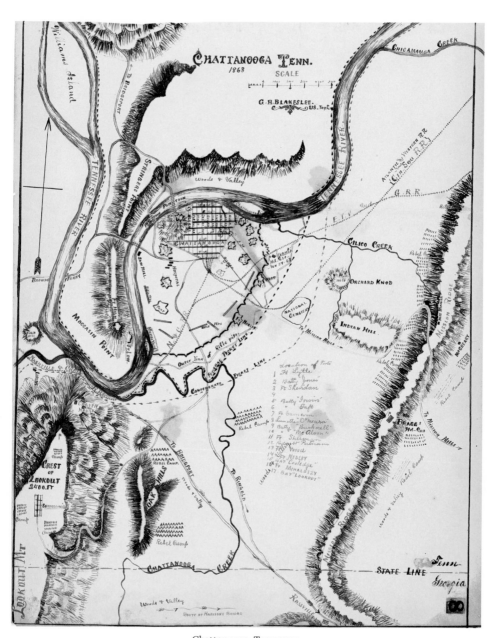

Chattanooga, Tennessee

Chapter 23   Chattanooga

By May 10th, I successfully travelled as far south as Chattanooga Tennessee. To my terrible dismay I found the regiment had left several days before I got there. I would have given anything to have got there sooner so I could be with the boys.

For several days I was very gloomy. To have come such a distance and gotten within spitting distance of my friends, then to have my hopes dashed in such a way was too much for my spirits.

I prayed that we were to soon shove on to where ever the regiment lay but the orders were countermanded and we travelers were set down tight in the city. Sherman was pushing the enemy down into Georgia and was said to have sent a dispatch saying not to send more troops until he ordered it. I began to fear I would not ever cetch up to my friends after all.

Chattanooga was at least in some respects pleasantly situated. It reminded me somewhat of Harpers Ferry, surrounded by mountains and located on a beautiful river winding its way among them.

Around May 12th we heard the booming of cannon. We learnt of a battle raging[1] at a distance of some twenty miles away. Hundreds of wounded from my old 12th Corps, now called the 20th, soon began to pour into the city.

I expected again at any minute to be given arms and called to the front. I trusted that I was prepared for any event, even my own death as I placed myself once again in God's hands. I just wanted to have a gun for I didn't fancy meeting those rebel hell hounds on uneven ground. If I had a gun I would never surrender to be butchered. We had all heard of prisoners being killed outright on account of reb cruelty, that and the rebs having nothing left to feed captives. A man's life was not looked upon as of much account down there. If a man should drop dead, the crowd would hardly look about to see him. But, Chattanooga was strongly fortified and I didn't think it could be taken by rebs in any respect.

After several days, they had us set up camp by the river as though in a regiment. Hooker and the 20th were on the move with Sherman[2] and they said we could not reach him even if we tried. I determined that I had to handle my disappointment and take things cool. An officer came along naming me the company clerk and I was sent straight over to work in the Medical Director's offices.

We fared well enough for those days spent in Chattanooga, living under the foot of Lookout Mountain on an old rebel camp ground. From the top of the mountain, they said a man could see off into eight different states, it was that high up. There was still not a jot to be read coming from my friends out at the front.

One day, a group of us went to the river for a swim. While going there we passed through one of our burying grounds and also one of the rebs' where the graves dot the ground as though they were potato hills. We passed also through a village cemetery, which had been riddled by shells. We went into a large vault which wasn't fastened and was some shattered. It contained five bodies in metallic coffins which we lifted the covers from and under the glass covers, the skeletons were to be plainly seen. I felt bad as it was a sad sort of amusement.

We had no news from the fight as the news was suppressed but a great many rebs started to show up among us saying they took the opportunity to desert or surrender when they had a chance. They were awful discouraged by events in Georgia.

I heard at that time from brother Ed back in New York that he was in fine fettle although smallpox had broke out on David's Island not long after I left and they were under a quarantine for many weeks. Quite a few of the doctors and other staff died but he and Birdsey come through unscathed.

Then a Lieutenant Colonel from our regiment showed up wounded in the left arm, though slight. He said the regiment hadn't seen any hard fighting up until the time of his injury. Only one killed and ten wounded so far. I was grateful for his news as I worried so constantly over the fate of my friends.

Five rebel surgeons also came to report to the hospital to take care of their own men that come in. They had been captured the other day.

One of them, come into our offices, said to the Medical Director, "Doc, I heard we had one hundred and fifty of our Corps taken prisoner."

The Director said, "It is not so." The reb turned around and said, "Well that is a very pleasant surprise."

From the tone of the scamp, I wanted to give him a clip on his chin.

From what I had talked with reb prisoners and heard from them, I should have felt free to say that at present, the enemy confronting our own noble army of western men mostly, who will fight like tigers, was about fifty thousand, and not over that. I was confident we would beat the rebs, having a much larger force. Our only fear was that Lee would fall back our way but as I said, Chattanooga was so fortified as to be near impregnable, even against General Lee and his troops.

Everyday, the city contained a vaster amount of human suffering. Hundreds of our brave boys came in maimed, crippled, and sick. There was a great deal of rain which made the conditions worse, harder on everyone.

Most of us there in different capacities like myself for instance began to suffer once more from acute diarrhea. I got very poorly again. My heart bothered me a good deal with palpitations and bouts of weakness. I thought it most likely to render me unfit for field service tho I still hoped to be called up.

I got to feeling so very bad that I had difficulties not giving in to the dangerous temptations and evil influences that were everywhere for a soldier in Chattanooga. It seemed the life of the human body could not live without refreshing itself from the many things God has so bounteously furnished. And yet, the soul could not live in Christ and prepare itself for eternity if it partook of that bounty, but must necessarily be cold to the un-Christian life. It was a matter of great confusion to me at times such as those.

By the end of the month of May, I still lived but my being was somewhat emaciated again. I performed my duties in the office though I was reduced to skin and bone.

Then the weather grew exceedingly warm. Luckily, frequent showers brought some refreshment. I began to mend a little from the attentions of the Sanitary Commission which had recently established itself in the city. They came right to the front and distributed luxuries, like clean clothing and healthy victuals, to our brave boys. It was an institution beloved by all the soldiers.

I was also able to occasionally attend a religious meeting which I enjoyed.

Work to fortify the city continued constantly around us. There were four regiments of negroes working diligently at it.

I met quite a few local citizens. I can attest that the young ladies of Tennessee chawed tobacco, smoked, and rode horseback with their lovers on one horse! If I went into a house, the women and even the little chicks would all beg for chaw tobacco. The populace seemed mostly very ignorant. I thought the country would be fine if it had the enterprise of the North. Slavery had kept it down, most all its people poorly educated.

The fighting to the south of us in Georgia was terrible. We heard that Sherman had taken Atlanta[3], and then we heard that he had not. Wounded were carried in a constant river past the office where I sat, making out long lists of their names for the newspapers.

By now, we had seven reb doctors in the place where we dined. They had a little table by themselves. Those surgeons had cups and saucers while we had none. We were going to get up a petition against it and send it and claim that we should have as good as rebels at least.

On June 3rd, I got the bad news that the 107th had seen one of the sharpest engagements it ever had. It had been cut up very bad, 148 being the number said to be killed and wounded. I went out that night and found a good many of them as they came in. All I found were minus a leg or arm and some both. I found nine or ten. The slight wounded we sent on by rail to Nashville to the hospitals up there. None of my boys was among them, thank God, but it was hard to imagine how many able bodied men were still left in the regiment.

The next afternoon, I found one of our officers, Captain Laslie, from the 107th lying in one of the wards which I pass going to my meals. He knew me in a moment and we had a very cordial greeting. He gave me the welcome news that all my friends, Tenbrook, Wiggins, Edgerton, and some others I knew were definitely safe.

He told me the place they had fought at so hard at was called Hope Church. The boys that were still in the regiment vowed they were bound to revenge the death of their noble comrades who had fallen. Their only wish was to be let loose upon the rebs the sooner the better for their blood was up and they were loaded for bear. Laslie told me that the boys had fought like tigers never flinching an inch. I would to Heaven I were able to undergo the marching so I might be with them.

Laslie had his right leg taken off five inches above the knee. He was doing well in spite of it. I went into the city and got some dried fruit of different kinds, some condensed milk, crackers, & such from the Sanitary on my own hook for him. He was very thankful. I stayed with him till late, fanning him to sleep as it was very hot

277

and he suffered from that fact. I went to see him each morning and again at night. I tried to do all I could for the boys I found.

The Captain told me I couldn't stand it in the regiment in my present condition and did not think I should go back if called. He said I did more for the cause where I was than I could do back in the field. Also, I could have his influence and he would do anything for me in his power, for he said he could not repay me for my kindness to him. After his telling me that, I felt somewhat less bothered about my situation.

Then his wife came down from home and we rigged them up a tent which they lived in and it made things very pleasant for the Captain.

Mrs. Laslie was a fine woman. I knew it would come very beneficial to the Captain's health, her being there. Not every wife would leave her little children and start out at the news of her husband's misfortunes, come right to the seat of war, encountering inconveniences that many a man shirks from. I hoped I had chosen such a woman in Amy. But I had heard nothing in a long time from New York State. It was as though that place had been swallowed up by a volcano or something of the kind.

Once Dr. Flood came into Chattanooga from the regiment with a number of our men. He and the hospital steward of the regiment stayed with me until the night they went back. They all said that I looked hard and advised me to stay away from the regiment.

The good doctor gave me a certificate of competency for the position of steward, saying I was not of physical constitution to endure field service. I had lost twenty pounds in the last month over which time it had rained almost constantly and made for an unhealthy situation in Chattanooga and down in Atlanta where Dr. Flood told me the regiment now lay entrenched outside that city in a siege.

At least the news from the regiment was still good. Tenbrook was alright, tough as nails as usual. They said Wiggins was a better soldier than he formerly was, but he had got so that he swore like a pirate.

∞

1. Resaca

On May 13th, 1864, the Battle of Resaca began about 30 miles south of Chattanooga. Sherman started the battle by staging the first flank attack against a well-fortified rebel position at the town of Dalton, Georgia. The success of this effort led the rebel General Johnston to fall back for 13 miles and look for new ground on which to take a stand. He chose very unwisely, stringing his regiments out in a series of barely defensible positions through the town of Resaca.

For a brief time, Sherman had a wide open opportunity to attack and destroy Johnston's weakly arranged army, but like so many Union generals before him he faltered at this key juncture and subsequently decided to entrench artillery rather than strike immediately. In retrospect it looked as though Sherman could have ended the campaign then and there, practically in one day, if he had just struck fast enough.

General Williams' Division, which still included the boys of the 107th NY, engaged with the Confederates commanded by General Hood on the final day of fighting, clashing as each side sought to advance, fighting on awful ground composed for the most part of steep ravines and thick bushes. Williams managed to surprise a large force of rebels and defeat them with a flank attack and a brisk exchange. He was satisfied with the division's performance after their long period of inactivity and stated proudly "they behaved splendidly. Not a man left the ranks unless wounded."

Ruger's brigade managed to capture the flag, several officers, and over one hundred infantrymen from the 38th Alabama regiment, in what the men also called 'a splendid fight.' General Knipe's brigade made a particularly effective advance upon an enemy position. He and his nephew, a member of his staff, were unfortunately wounded that day. Knipe's injury was slight but his young nephew died of his wounds. Knipe was able to resume his duties within a week.

Williams estimated that over three days of hostilities he lost between 4 and 5 hundred men, either killed, wounded, or missing. As usual the Division received no credit in the press for their accomplishments.

Though General Williams led his Division to victory, the clash between the two armies was deemed a draw in the end.

The outcome has been called a Confederate tactical victory but one without much satisfaction or noticeable advantage, for Sherman managed to keep up a series of flanking threats after the battle that forced General Johnston to pull his men out of their entrenched positions in Resaca and fall back to protect the railroad south of town, a case of maneuver warfare triumphing over frontal attacks. The all important life line that connected the rebel army to Atlanta had to remain in Johnston's hands if there was to be any hope of stalling the Union advance.

The battle at Resaca would prove to have in it all the elements that would define the way the campaign was to play out over the next 4 long months. Meeting there for the first time, the two commanders and their armies revealed their personal strengths and weaknesses.

2. Sherman's March to the Sea

A day after the battle at Resaca, William's Division was already on the move again, called away so quickly that they could not finish burying the rebel dead who lay scattered around in the woods along what had been the front line.

Marching many miles to the south into Georgia, Edgerton wrote about how the regiment kept up a steady pace of chasing rebels. General Williams described a typical day for his daughter. "I was ordered to the front til I met the enemy. We drove his skirmishers before us over hills and down valleys, across creeks and marshes until after dusk when I halted and bivouacked, sleeping myself under a very dense thicket."

The men of his Division were tired but behaved well until May 20th, when they arrived near a small town called Cassville. Williams sent 2 regiments into the town to occupy it.

When they got there they found it had been totally deserted by its inhabitants. They also discovered to their dismay that rebs were entrenched nearby on a hill overlooking the town and soon Williams' men found themselves under a barrage of nasty artillery fire that pinned them down. Nerves frayed, frustrations erupted, and quite suddenly the men ran wild.

They set fire to principal buildings and pillaged every house.

Williams had to bring in other regiments to take out the enemy battery on the hill and then put out the spreading fires and restore order. But it was too late; almost everything in the town was burned, broken or dragged away as plunder. When the infantry looted a town and civilians' homes it was considered a lapse of discipline and Williams was not happy with his men. It was a serious blot on his Division's previously excellent record.

Ironically, when a general ordered a town or city burnt in the name of destroying resources that might be aiding the war effort, it was much more acceptable, seen as an unfortunate but necessary consequence of waging war by the aggressor. It was called a 'Scorched Earth' policy.

General Sherman would judge it necessary to put a match to a large portion of the city of Atlanta on November 4th as part of his campaign to break the heart of the Confederacy. Although it was not his intention to burn down the civilian neighborhoods and businesses, many of them caught fire regardless.

Because of the burning of Atlanta Sherman's name went down in the South's book of infamous persons and remains there today.

After the sacking of Cassville, the 20th Corps was granted a day of respite. While the men rested, the generals met with Hooker to discuss their progress.

And then on the 23rd, Williams got orders to prepare for another 20 day long march. They were off once again, marching through a tremendous storm of lightning, thunder, and rain, hard on the heels of the retreating rebel army. The citizens of Cassville crept home to their village and found ashes and splinters where their houses had once stood.

General Johnston decided that he must take another stand and resist the force that pursued his army so relentlessly. He stopped and dug in around the town of Dallas, GA. The next day, the 25th of May, the Union boys arrived on the scene and the Battle of New Hope Church was fought in the area.

At New Hope Church, General Williams division was engaged to advance upon the enemy entrenchments in a triple wave of brigades.

General Knipe, recovered from his wound, rode out with them. This maneuver was executed so beautifully that Hooker, watching from a hillside, declared it to be the most "magnificent sight of the entire war!" That in all his experience, he had never seen anything as splendid.

Williams' pride in his troops was restored. But, it came at a price; he greatly regretted that he lost over 800 of them that day.

The 107th NY itself suffered around 150 casualties; as Rufus described it, "they were all cut to pieces." Luckily Wiggins, Edgerton, and Will Tenbrook managed to come through unscathed.

Edgerton wrote proudly of the battle to his mother, saying: "I have passed through another battle safe and sound, did my duty like a true soldier. General Hooker was just behind our regiment when we was fighting under a shower of bullets and grape shot and said that he never saw a regiment do as well or fight as bravely before, that is what he told our colonel, it was the hottest place I was ever in, our regiment lost 168 killed and wounded but I am safe and sound, not a scratch although men was shot down on both sides of me."

Once again, incredibly, the national press gave the credit to another division and another general. Williams was indignant. He wanted his men given the acclaim they deserved for their beautifully executed charge.

After the battle, a standoff of 5 days ensued between the armies, with a high level of constant fire from sharpshooters and skirmishers that kept everyone on edge and unable to sleep.

As the month of May drew to a close, Rufus received inaccurate news of the battle at New Hope Church and of what was going on at the front. But casualties from the battle began pouring back into Chattanooga; these injured men would fill him in on the true details of the fight over the days to come.

3. Atlanta

By the last week in June, Sherman's army at last reached the outskirts of Atlanta. They had had a very rough time getting there.

Since the Battle at New Hope Church, Sherman kept up his advance along the railroad toward Atlanta and General Johnston fought to stop him at every turn. It rained for weeks on end, making life miserable for the boys in the field. The two armies engaged in this Atlanta Campaign moved together in such close proximity that along with the rain, the sound of gunfire never ceased as the days wore on. Wet clothes, constant gunfire, exposure, and exhaustion took a toll on everyone's state of mind in the 20th Corps.

Soon, General Williams noticed an unusual phenomenon beginning along his picket lines.

The enemy pickets were so close at hand that a Union man could easily shout out a 'hail' and start up conversation. Mutually sick of the endless hostilities, the pickets began to organize truces with each other.

Williams described the situation in his letters: "For the last few days our pickets have completely fraternized. They have been exchanging papers, coffee, tobacco, and the like. Yesterday morning I found them actually sitting together on the banks of a small stream, a branch of the Allatoona Creek. I was obliged to stop the fraternal intercourse. Isn't it strange that men in mortal strife one hour are on affectionate terms the next! and apparently fast friends. Strange are the commingled events and incidents of war!"

The 107th NY Regiment put in breastworks and entrenchments less than a mile from the rebel army near Marietta, Georgia, just outside Atlanta. They had been under fire since the 25th of May without letup. Edgerton called the campaign 'a campaign of hardships,' and described 'being wet to the skin for upwards of 70 hours, marching, sleeping, and skirmishing in the mud and rain.' He found it a wonder that he was still alive.

Williams sadly figured that over 1200 of his men were now missing from the ranks, lost in the fighting and marching since leaving Chattanooga.

View of the Tennessee River from Lookout Mountain

Sherman's March

Train Wreck

Chapter 24   Lookout Mountain

While I labored over my forms in the medical director's office as clerk, the weather finally turned clear in June. The army had begun to build a large new hospital to accommodate thousands of men. It was to be up on the hillside of Lookout Mountain where patients could be safe. I learnt I myself was to be transferred up there soon.

Affairs in the city were peaceful enough. But, guerrilla warfare continued to torment the countryside outside of Chattanooga. Bridges burnt, trains run off, and men slaughtered almost every day by contemptible villains who hadn't the honor of an uncivilized Indian.

A sneaking band of guerrillas attacked a post between the city and Nashville one day. There were fourteen of our boys very plucky and wouldn't give up. They were all killed, some hung, others shot. After that, when our boys captured any of the guerrillas, they shot them on the spot. That was the way they were served now who were caught guerilla-ing.

Around this time, one of our most useful spies was killed in our area. I used to see him with Hooker on the Potomac. We reckoned back then he was a prisoner as he had on a rebel general's uniform and yet some said he was a spy and so it seemed for he came along down here and was put on General Grant's staff as chief of the spies. They say he had eighty-five suits of clothes. Many times he went right into the rebel lines as one of their generals and even took command of a body of their troops. He would take other spies along with him and give them passes to go snooping through the reb army.

The rebs were offering $15,000 for him dead or alive, yet they had never been able to nab him. Then a lady nearby coyed him off to her house fourteen miles from here, and her husband shot him.

Of course, our boys went out and their property was destroyed and those folks taken care of.

In July they moved my place of abode up the mountain and put me in as chief drug dispenser in the new hospital apothecary. It was a lofty spot, a beautiful place to live and work and I was much obliged. The atmosphere was so pure and healthy I thought I would get as fat as a pig and feel topnotch in no time.

From up there the trees down in Chattanooga looked like running blackberry bushes. It rained in the valley quite often and I could see the lightning and hear the thunder almost directly underneath us. The white clouds below would come rolling along in huge waves mountain high and as far as the eye could reach. It was glorious, completely obscuring the view of the valley below, yet above us the sky was blue and fine. Then the clouds might take on a darker look and perhaps a fearful storm would burst out around us on the hill.

The Tennessee River wound its way like a silver street around the foot of the mountain, thence up among the numerous other mounts of Tennessee and was finally lost to view. I compared it to quick silver gliding rapidly while it cut its bed a chasm of beauty in my letters but I could not be a poet anymore than a sheep could be a goat. I was not homesick or discontented when I was surrounded by the gracious bounties of God and the sublime workings of nature which were all around me manifested. In addition it was very cool and pleasant up there. I could go out and pick blackberries and huckleberries not but a hundred or two rods from the hospital.

My younger brother George wrote to me to say he desired me to get him a "shooting iron" and he was very taken by the idea of becoming a soldier.

I answered him back to leave such missiles alone, for once he'd come to the reality of using them in earnest he would feel different. I told him to get no notions of war into his head but to be a good Christian boy and get a good education, for if he did, when he became a man he could do anything he wanted. I said I would learn him the drug business when I got home if he wanted a trade. I could tolerate no further talk from my family of any one of them getting into the war, for I had seen enough of its terrible effects on both mind and body.

Luckily for me, the healthful style of life on the mountain gave me some respite from the miseries of a war torn nation. For a brief time, I enjoyed a sort of time out of time, living quite literally above it all. I think back on those busy but tranquil days as the quiet before another storm that was to soon overtake me.

My duties on Lookout were the same as before only even more arduous as I had to train two new men. I was the only one who knew anything of hospital affairs. Then the two, who were becoming good druggists, got beastly drunk and were sent off back to their regiments in disgrace. I was left fully in charge of all the business and had to step to.

At long last, Tenbrook got a letter through to me written on the 24th of August. He wrote: "Once more I sit down in the trenches to write a few lines to an old friend and tent mate on whom the fortunes of war have been less severe than on myself. Still I cannot complain as I have never had a scratch from a rebel bullet or shell."

My friends were living like soldiers, under the breastworks around Atlanta[1] with cannonballs, flying over their heads. Edgerton had taken a bullet to the shoulder from a sharpshooter as he went off to cook breakfast one time. Will then spent a few days in the division hospital.

Wiggins said he was lucky the wound was slight. Edgerton told Tenbrook when he returned to the regiment that he felt like he was ninety-nine years old by now and was completely played out after all their ordeals, though he had only just turned nineteen.

Also, Tenbrook and Wiggins had come down with the soldiers curse again. He called it "the shits" though he apologized to me for the shock of his vulgar parlance. Wiggins had got quite sick for a spell but was now getting well enough to eat all his own rations and Tenbrook's too so they knew he would get along. Of course, Wiggins was always big as life and full of talk as usual.

Tenbrook further explained that their skirmish line was within short musket range of the rebel forts in the suburbs of the city so they had made a compromise with the rebs directly in front of them not to fire at each other.

Will wrote that every night, their Division band went up on the hill just behind them and played for all to hear. Shelling in the area would immediately stop and men called out for their favorite tunes from both sides. When the serenade finished, the cannons resumed their pounding sending lovely arcs of fire into the doomed city. It looked just like fireworks at home, he said.

During those summer days on the mountain, I remembered my many conversations with George Wood. He certainly thought I had the makings of a surgeon if I worked hard at it. So, I took up once again my study of medicine. I had the opportunity to witness all the operations & such. I also assisted in postmortems in the dead house. The doctors spared no pains during those operations to slice up pretty well their subjects. I once cut my finger to the bone with a knife used in gangrene. I drew the poison from the incision with my mouth and it did not impart any into the wound. Such scenes aroused my deepest curiosity, as if the whole of the life and death of a human body was a mystery to be unraveled.

On September 3rd we finally got the glorious news that Atlanta was OURS!

We were elated, literally prancing through our work that day. But quick on the uplifting word from Atlanta, there transpired an event that altered the bearings by which I held fast to my world, throwing my private soul into the darkest state of confusion and anxiety.

∽

1. Atlanta

The night of September 1st, 1864 the Federal Army's major push into Atlanta began. The rebel forces responded by blowing up their ammunition depots in the city. The horizon glowed red all through the dark hours.

The 107th NY was called away from picket duty on the river and the next day, Sept 2, was given the honor of being one of the first of four regiments that marched into Atlanta on reconnaissance. They found they were unopposed except by a squad of rebel cavalry who they drove before them without much difficulty.

Members of the 107th NY reported that the retreating rebels had left widespread destruction in their wake, hoping to leave nothing useful behind them, and that the many weeks of shelling had left much of the city in ruins. Hardly a house did not show signs of war damage. Edgerton said it was "a desolate looking place…with as much as a quarter of it burned down."

In the less damaged residential parts of town, some families had dug caves in their gardens and furnished them with their household goods. They had been living underground during the long weeks of the siege. Now they wandered aimlessly in the streets or gathered on their porches to eye the occupiers with hostility and suspicion.

The 3rd of September, church bells rang out through the occupied town, but though it seemed that peace had come at last, Sherman soon gave out orders that the citizens should make plans to leave. There was not enough food or supplies left for his army let alone to support a civilian population.

Chapter 25   Stonewall

The next big event of my war years began without warning. I was taken entirely by surprise. This is what transpired.

We pill boys had our own table in the doctors' mess up at the new hospital on the mountainside, and plenty of good food provided too. Nigh to us was a table that held four of the rebel doctors there to help see to their own boys. They kept to themselves the most of the time and were usually quiet. But other times we overheard their talk if we cared to listen in. Of course, we were curious to know all about them so we frequently bent an ear in their direction.

One dinner time, their conversation turned to a discussion of the Battle at Gettysburg and they grew quite animated. I clearly heard one of them exclaim bitterly that Robert E. Lee had said plain as day that he would have beat the Army of the Potomac if he still had Stonewall by his side to help him do it at Gettysburg, and so he could have won the war for the Southern cause.

It was just as I thought so too, and I knew many more agreed with me on this point.

One of the other reb doctors ventured that he knew the man who had been Stonewall's personal physician[1] and had cared for the fallen general in his dying days near the Chancellorsville battlefield.

When I heard these words, I lent in a bit closer for I had always kept up a strong interest in Stonewall Jackson and his death, having been a close witness to his brilliant flank attack.

The doctor went on to say this friend of his was there the whole time from when the General was shot that fateful night and he had amputated Stonewall's arm at a farmhouse, until the very morning Stonewall passed on with himself and many other doctors standing around helpless to do a thing about it, a full ten days later.

Stonewall's doctor had thought that after his arm was off the General might come through, and it seemed at first that he would. But then after some days of improvement, he had taken poorly again and died. Perhaps because he had lost so much blood or perhaps he had caught a contagion of the belly that would not let him live.

The conversation at the table continued on for some time about what the actual cause of death might have been. There was some confusion on this point.

Then I heard one doctor say, "I heared he was kilt by his own men[2], is that a fact?"

"Yes," says the original story teller, "Its a fact. His boys from Carolina didn't know that there were two parties of officers, including Stonewall hisself and other generals, out on the road afore 'em, ridin' reconnaissance into the night. I'm guessin' Stonewall wanted his men to be startin' up the advance agin' but somethin' was holdin' em back so he goes on ahead to see what was up for hisself. Got too far out there, I reckon. His aides said they were atryin' to tell him it were too dangerous but he was a determined man and the front was quieted down besides. He'd sent out skirmishers around the area as a precaution, they said. Most determined man ever there was. Y'all know its true. Couldn't done half of what he done if he warent."

I saw out of the corner of my own eye how the other three doctors nodded sadly in agreement.

"Then," continues on the speaker, "they say some fool yank boys come poppin' up out of a thicket. Just stumbles outa the bushes alongside the road, lost behind our lines. One of them damn fools up and fires a shot at the general's party."

His words froze the very air inside my chest into shards of ice. My heart felt like it stopped its beating in a terrible cramp. I couldn't cetch my breath for anything.

For I knew in an instant the identity of the damn fool he was was talking about!

I was that very same man. It had to have been me!

The shot, my one lonesome shot fired that night in my over wrought state, against General Knipe's strict orders. The shot I let off at the shadowy riders in the road who bore down upon us out of that gloomy red moonlight. The shot I fired for some reason I could barely name in panic, obeying a frightened urge I couldn't contain.

The doctor went on with his explanation of the fatal night's events. Unaware how I now hung on every word. It was if I were drowning. I tried to start up my breathing again without alerting the other pill boys at the table to my rising state of distress.

"They say a few more of those yanks let off a volley at the general's party. No one knows if any of their bullets hit Stonewall because other firing started off on account of being set off by those damn yanks who shouldn't a been anywhere near there, what with our skirmishers supposed to have swept the area."

"The reconnaissance parties then turned round to run lickety-split back toward our lines but a regiment of Stonewall's own boys from North Carolina went down on their knees and shot the generals and all their staff by mistake. Thought they were shootin' at yankee cavalry comin' at them outta the dark. By the time they brought in Stonewall, he was hit three times and practically bled to death. My friend, Doc McGuire, well he said the general had barely any pulse left."

Another of the reb docs, shook his head and said in a mournful voice, "You know it was the greatest tragedy for our cause. I would not give a thousand dollars for the life of the captain from North Carolina who gave that order to fire. May God forgive him is all I can say, for I cannot."

"Amen to that, brother, they say he is a broken man," said the story teller. "The aides told my friend that the General's men

293

were all yellin' not to shoot but that poor captain took it for a dirty yank trick and told his boys to go on and 'lay it into them!'"

I could not bear to hear another word. Trembling with shock, I stood and carefully walked myself from the room and went to sit upon my bed. I was filled with dread for what I had done. I replayed over and over the terrible scene of that night. It fit with what the reb doc had described in every particular.

Dear Lord, I had truly done it. I had either shot Stonewall or caused him to be shot down during that fearsome night in the woods and I had never even knowed of it till this shocking moment. My lonesome shot had set off events practically causing the Confederates to be losing the war.

Guilt and shame flooded through me. Stonewall was the noblest of Christian men, as I have related. To have caused such a man to die was a thought too horrible and confusing for my youthful mind to absorb. I could see it as both a cowardly act or as almost completely contrary to that. The mysterious nature of my feelings confounded me at every turn.

I quickly determined that I must reveal to no one my guilt in committing this act or I would sacrifice my safety. I feared that if it were known, I would be killed, either by a rebel patient right there in the hospital, or by a Copperhead snake. There were men out there who would surely not rest if they knew it was I had led to the downfall of their great hero.

In the weeks following this awful discovery, I crept about my business like a man stricken once again by concussion and torn by invisible bullets.

294

1. Stonewall's Doctor

Dr. McGuire was Stonewall Jackson's personal doctor. He wrote an extended and detailed account of Stonewall's death after the war recounting how he came out to the battlefield to collect Jackson in an ambulance and found his friend in very poor condition from blood loss. The general was hemorrhaging from the most severe wound, the one in the left arm just below the shoulder.

Luckily Dr. McGuire was able to insert his finger into the bullet hole and pinch off the artery. He reported that Stonewall was calm, polite, and unafraid, which revealed to McGuire evidence of a superior mind and soul well in command of himself.

Dr. McGuire gave his stoic patient morphia and whiskey before loading him into a wagon and moving him to a tavern behind the front lines. After examining his wounds, Dr. McGuire determined that Jackson's arm needed to be amputated as soon as possible. The bone had been completely shattered by the bullet. Surgery took place just after 2 am and Jackson remained under the effects of chloroform through the rest of the night. In the morning, a chaplain took the severed limb to a peaceful farm a mile away and buried it under a marker for posterity.

Jackson regained consciousness when a courier arrived. The courier asked if Jackson had any special instructions for the day's battle. Jackson at first seemed to rally and made an effort to reply but then fell back and only weakly managed to say, "I don't know - I can't tell; say to General Stuart he must do what he thinks is best."

Later in the day, Jackson dictated a note to General Lee congratulating him on the successful attack he had just made on the Chancellorsville House and Union headquarters. General Lee wrote back:

"Could I have directed events, I should have chosen for the good of the country to be disabled in your stead. I congratulate you upon the victory, which is due to your skill and energy."

Then Lee ordered that Jackson be moved to a safer spot where he would be out of range of shells and any possibility of capture, should the fortunes of the rebel army change.

Jackson was taken to the home of a friend of his, a Mr. Chandler, at a place called Guiney's Station. The main house at Chandler's farm was already filled with casualties, so they installed the General in a smaller house on the property where he might have privacy and quiet.

Jackson's condition improved in the comfort and peace of his surroundings at first. He seemed to be in good spirits and recovery from the amputation looked to be straightforward. His wife and young daughter were called for. Then, sadly, several days later, just before his wife was able to get there, he began to complain of acute abdominal pain and show signs of having what was thought to be pneumonia.

Lee could not bear this turn for the worse and would almost not hear of it. He wrote to the Chaplain, " Give him my affectionate regards and tell him to make haste and get well, and come back to me as soon as he can. He has lost his left arm, but I have lost my right."

Though people all over the South prayed for Jackson's recovery, and his wife arrived to nurse him tirelessly, along with a veritable army corps of doctors, his health relentlessly declined.

"When his child was brought to him Saturday," Dr. McGuire wrote, "he played with it for some time; frequently caressing it and calling it his 'little comforter.' At one time he raised his wounded hand above his head and, closing his eyes, was for some moments silently engaged in prayer. He said to me:

"I see from the number of physicians that you think my condition dangerous, but I thank God, if it is His will, that I am ready to go.'"

About daylight Sunday morning on the 10th of May, Mrs. Jackson felt that she had best inform her husband that his recovery was very doubtful, and that it was better that they both prepare for the worst. He was silent for a moment and then said:

"It will be infinite gain to be translated to Heaven."

He still expressed some faint hope of recovery, but requested of her, if he should die, to have him buried in Lexington in the valley of Virginia. His exhaustion increased so rapidly that by 11 am, a tearful Mrs. Jackson knelt by his bed and told him that before the sun went down he would be with his beloved Savior. He replied, trying to reassure her:

"Oh, no! you are frightened, my child; death is not so near; I may yet get well."

She fell over the bed weeping and told him again that the physicians said there was no hope for his survival. Stonewall bore this news thoughtfully and then wanted to speak to McGuire, asking him, "Doctor, Anna informs me that you have told her that I am to die today; is it so?"

When the doctor told him that this was the truth, Stonewall raised his eyes to the ceiling and seemed to accept his fate with great dignity; he turned to his wife and the doctors and said, "Very good, very good, it is all right."

Then he began to speak quietly to his wife, trying to say all the things he needed to say before weakness overtook him. A little later, he rallied enough to add, 'It is the Lord's day; my wish is fulfilled. I have always desired to die on Sunday.'

Doctor Mcguire described that in his last hour, "His mind now began to fail and wander, and he frequently talked as if in command upon the field, giving orders in his old way; then the scene shifted, and he was at the mess table in conversation with members of his staff, now with his wife and child; now at prayers with his military family. Occasional intervals of his mind would appear, and during one of them I offered him some brandy and water, but he declined the same, saying: "'It will only delay my departure, and do no good; I want to preserve my mind, if possible, to the last.'"

In his final moments, with complete clarity and a look of sweet expectation upon his face, the great general said: "Let us cross over the river, and rest under the shade of the trees." "And then," the doctor tells us, " without pain, or the least struggle, his spirit passed from earth to the God who gave it."

Whether Stonewall Jackson was describing the heavenly place he was bound for or the revered bend in the river by the mill buildings of his childhood, his mourners could not tell. His last words have become one of the most famous death bed utterances in American history.

His body was driven down to Richmond where it lay in state for a steady stream of mourners. The young and old came to pay their respects. He was buried in Lexington, Virginia as he had wished.

2. Killed By His Own Men

Stonewall Jackson believed fervently that once you had your enemy on the run, you did not give him a second to catch his breath and possibly take a stand. You kept the pressure on. You made him run until he could run no more and only stopped to fall to his knees and surrender his weapons.

The night of May 2nd, at Chancellorsville, Stonewall grew impatient that his brilliant flank attack had come to a halt. He began to take steps to get it moving again. And he did it in his typical way, forcefully and in person.

He rode out among his troops, ordering officers left and right to restore discipline to their commands and press forward as soon as possible.

As his men struggled to get back into battle lines, it became apparent that many of them needed to rest. Jackson realized that the level of confusion was so high that setting up the lines of the leading brigades was going to be impossible to accomplish. He therefore ordered a powerful brigade of North Carolinians who had been held in reserve during the day to move forward and take up a position in the very front. This was General Lane's Brigade made up of 5 regiments from General A.P. HIll's Division of Jackson's Corps.

Stonewall had it in his mind to drive his line of advance all the way to the Chancellorsville House and more importantly to capture the roads that led northward to the river fords. He meant to cut the Union army off both from its supply route and its way home. Nothing less than complete victory held his attention. The fresh troops from North Carolina were going to help him lead the way.

He had 8 men riding with him that night; they were his aides, other staff, and a guide. Jackson wanted to know what was still holding up the pace of his advance, but in particular, why his line of skirmishers was not making any more progress in their move toward the Chancellorsville House. He was frustrated and impatient to get moving again. And he was sure that federal troops had fled from the area. So he and his staff rode out beyond the lines of the North Carolinians into the dark along the Orange Plank Road.

There was little reason for Jackson to put himself at risk and in such an advanced position out beyond his own lines at Chancellorsville except for his determination and his hands on approach to providing his men with inspirational leadership.

These characteristics had served him well in the past, providing him with drive, obstinacy, and his legendary strength. Now these very qualities, coupled with his impatience, blurred his judgment. Frustrated members of Jackson's staff nervously told the general that he was putting himself in too much danger, but he waved them off and went ahead, riding his favorite horse, Little Sorrel, up the road. After all it was quiet. There was no shooting going on.

Some 60 yards behind General Jackson's group another party of officers also travelled out along the turnpike. This one was composed of General A. P. Hill and his staff. General Hill said later that he went along because he felt it his duty to accompany and possibly provide protection for his commander. He had 9 men riding along with him.

Jackson's group started forward on the Turnpike but then they turned up a dirt road to the left, a smaller track called the Mountain Road which ran parallel to the Plank Road, separated from it by a thin strip of light woods about 150 feet wide. At some point, they had passed, practically unnoticed in the dark, through the front lines of the 18th NC.

This track was ostensibly a safer route for Jackson to take as the main road had come recently under Union cannon fire. Also Jackson was most interested in taking a look in the direction that led Northeast toward the road to the river crossings. The fords still remained one of his primary targets.

General Hill's party continued to ride straight along the momentarily quiet turnpike. His group made their way forward, also passing by the ranks of the 18th NC. The men in the 18th NC regiment again barely noticed General Hill and his men in the dim moonlight. None of the officers in the regiment had been clearly informed that there were going to be generals riding out beyond them on reconnaissance missions. In fact most of them had been ordered to stay on alert for a possible surprise attack by federal cavalry.

The generals got 3 or 4 hundred yards out beyond their front lines. Stonewall Jackson, in the lead on the Mountain Road, stopped his horse when he got near enough to hear the sounds of axes and voices ringing through the trees and realized how shockingly close he was to his own skirmishers and possibly the enemy.

He listened for a few minutes and then turned around and began to carefully retrace his steps. When he had gotten about halfway back along the Mountain Road, he started to turn as if to leave the track, perhaps to cut down to the main road. Just then that a single shot rang out in the silence and echoed through the dark woods.

Men across an arc of 100's of yards heard it. Most of the rebels agreed it came from the south side of the road, slightly to their front. It was the shot that Rufus fired against orders: the famous lone gunshot.

Accompanying Stonewall Jackson on his reconnaissance mission that night was a young corporal named David Kyle who had been called up from the ranks to act as Stonewall's guide.

Kyle had lived in the area as a boy and knew the land and its roads better than anyone. Even in the darkness he recognized where he was. He recorded a careful account of where Stonewall was when the single shot rang out. He wrote:

"We went down that old Mountain Road some 400 yards when we came in hearing of the Federals. We stayed there I should judge from 2 to 4 minutes when General Jackson turned his horse around and started back down the road we had come down. When we were about halfway back, he turned his horse toward the south facing the front of our line of battle. He started to leave the Old Mountain Road and just his horse's feet had cleared the edge of the road while his hind feet was still on the edge of the bank, there was a single shot fired...in an instant it was taken up, and nearer there were five or six shots...and then suddenly a large volley, as if from a Regiment."

As the two parties of Confederate generals in the roads heard the first shot and then the volley, they all recognized the perilousness of their positions and turned their horses to gallop back to their own lines. Unfortunately, their own lines were not expecting them.

The men of the 18th North Carolinians thought the cavalry charge they had been warned about was materializing from the dark right in front of their eyes. Some of them even cried out, "Cavalry attack! Cavalry attack!" as a shadowy party of men galloped toward them out of the gloom on the turnpike. Some of them knelt, leveled their rifles and fired.

General Hill, whose party was by now only tens of yards in front of the 18th NC Regiment on the plank road, leapt down from his horse calling out "Cease Fire! Cease Fire!" as injured men and horses came crashing to the ground behind him.

Two of his men who did not fall were carried away by their terrified horses straight into the ranks of the enemy by the Chancellorsville House. Three officers in Hill's party had their horses killed under them, or in one's case over him. General Hill ran to try to pull his aide out from under the dying horse and probably saved his own life in the bargain by being so close to the ground.

This first round of bullets tore through Hill's group, flew through the woods, and then took a second toll on Jackson's group which was farther away, protected somewhat by the distance and the trees between them.

Jackson and his men bore less of the brunt of this first volley, but one man was killed instantly and others had their horses fall or bolt wildly out of control. Lieutenant Morrison, Stonewall's brother-in-law and one of his most devoted staff members, took a terrible fall from his horse but struggled to his feet and dashed toward the lines of the 18th NC screaming, "Stop! You are firing into your own men!"

It is not known if Jackson was already hit by the volley from the Federals or the first fuselage from his own men but Little Sorrel panicked and ran away with him into the woods. A low hanging oak branch struck Jackson viciously in the head and lacerated the side of his face. He was very nearly thrown from the saddle by the blow and in retrospect it would have been better if he had been so that he could have taken cover on the ground like General Hill.

Barely retaining his seat, he raised his right hand to fend off the boughs of the trees which continued to lash at him as little Sorrel plunged on through the thin strip of woods between the Mountain Road and the Turnpike.

Just then, Major Barry, a young rebel officer in charge of a part of the 18th NC's infantry line near the road, on hearing the cries for a cease fire from Lieutenant Morrison and still suspecting this was a Union cavalry charge, thought the calls to cease fire were a devious yankee trick. He yelled back "Who gave that order. He is a liar! Pour it into them boys!"

Following his instructions, the soldiers took aim and unleashed another, much deadlier round of bullets at the shadowy silhouettes thrashing through the woods in front of them.

This time Jackson was definitely hit. He had a wound to his right hand and two others in his left arm, both above and below the elbow. Little Sorrel, still panicking, ran on with his wounded rider through the brush to the edge of the turnpike where Major Wilbourn, another of Jackson's loyal staff officers, still on his own horse, caught up with the terrified animal and grabbed the reins that Stonewall could barely hold in his bleeding right hand. His other arm, the bone shattered below the shoulder, hung uselessly at his side.

Wilbourn looked back and saw by the light of the flashing muskets, men on their knees in a line, firing at them from about 40 yards away, the men of the 18th NC. They were in the classic infantry stance used to repel a cavalry charge.

The firing at last came to a halt as Lieutenant Morrison, his own shoulder badly injured from the fall from his horse, finally reached the infantry with his persistent cries for a cease fire. General Hill then stood up in the road and yelled furiously, "You have shot your friends! You have destroyed my staff!" He was the only one in his party to escape with his health and his horse intact; the rest were either dead, wounded, captured, or still pinned beneath their dying animals.

Stonewall Jackson sat upon Little Sorrel in a daze. He gazed with an expression of astonishment down the road and murmured to Major Wilbourn, "All my wounds are from my own men," as if he was struggling to accept this awful truth. Wilbourn replied, "They certainly seem to be our troops," and he saw Jackson nod.

While 9 out of 10 of Hill's party were either killed, wounded, or missing, only 3 in Jackson's party were hit by the wave of so called friendly fire, with just one killed outright. A total of five rounds had reached Stonewall and his men and unbelievably he had been hit by 3 of them. Of all of the 17 men in the two parties, the hero of Chancellorsville had been shot 3 times and lacerated across the face. His aides helped him from Little Sorrel and sat him down beneath a pine tree. General Hill rushed to his side and said, "General I hope you are not badly hurt," to which Jackson stoically replied that his arm was broken and that it was "very painful."

General Hill sat down and cradled Jackson's head in his lap. They took off Jackson's gauntlets and found them filled with blood but the wounds did not bleed excessively and no tourniquet was applied. Hill and Wilbourn bound the injuries as best they could and then fashioned a sling to hold the arm. A surgeon from the regiment came forward to help. As the little group attended their general more officers came out to offer aid until there were as many as a dozen men crowded around the fallen man.

Morrison went forward to a crest in the road to see what the yankees might be up to and saw that a Union battery was unlimbering not even a hundred yards away. Rushing back to the huddle around Jackson, he whispered that they must move him as soon as possible. General Hill ran back to his leaderless regiments to help them meet the artillery assault that could be expected at any moment.

Jackson thought that he could walk so Wilbourn and Morrison helped him to his feet and they began to make their slow and painful way back along the road toward their own lines.

Soon several soldiers came forward with a litter for Jackson. They placed him on it, hoisting it to their shoulders, and were able to move at a quicker pace toward safety but in the next moments the federal cannons behind them opened a terrible onslaught of fire. One of the litter bearers was hit twice and fell, almost dropping his corner of the litter. They put Jackson down as the cannons continued to rake the road with shot. Several of the entourage lay over Jackson to shield him with their bodies as he lay upon the ground.

Finally, during a lull in the firing, they got back up, put Jackson in the litter again and tried to hurry along through the woods instead of on the dangerous road. This time one of the bearers tripped over a root in the dark and Jackson rolled entirely out of the litter, landing hard on his left arm. The sharp fragments of broken bone likely ruptured an artery on impact. It was as though fate herself took a hand to finish what the men of the 18th NC had begun. The general burst into terrible groans. One of the bearers wrote," For the first time he groaned, and groaned piteously. He must have suffered excruciating agonies." In the dark and under fire, Jackson's litter bearers could not see that that their beloved general had started to bleed heavily through his bandage.

Again, the men picked Jackson up as tenderly as possible and carried him through the lines of infantry, trying to keep his identity a secret but a curious infantryman leaned in and recognized the general's face. He drew back in horror, exclaiming loudly for all to hear, "Great God, that's old General Jackson!"

The terrible news spread quickly. Within 10 minutes the men of the 18th NC knew what they had done. Major Barry never recovered from the shock and the shame of the order he had given that night. He died a young and broken hearted man 2 years after the war.

At last, Jackson's own doctor, Dr. Mcguire, met them with an ambulance wagon. "I am badly injured, Doctor," Jackson whispered in a calm voice, "I fear that I am dying." Mcguire gave him whiskey and morphine to dull his pain and noted later that the general "had lost a large amount of blood....and would have bled to death, but a tourniquet was immediately applied. For two hours he was nearly pulseless." The ambulance transported the sedated general to a hospital in the rear. Within hours, Mcguire would amputate Jackson's left arm just below the shoulder.

Last known photo of Stonewall Jackson, taken days before his wounding at Chancellorsville

Mourners at Stonewall's Grave

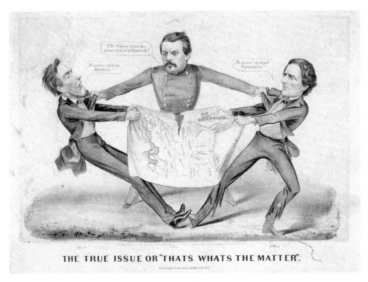

Election of 1864

McClellan Election Poster

Chapter 26   Diagnosis

I stayed on as druggist at the hospital on Lookout Mountain until October, keeping my head low all the while. I felt anxious that I was stuck fast in a tangled web of war and guilt that might never release me.

Then I was reassigned back down to the city of Chattanooga as chief clerk in the Federal Military Headquarters. I spent my days filling out large two and a half foot square reports, writing constantly. Sometimes I had to make four copies of each report, this keeping me very busy. I tried not to dwell upon the conversation overheard in the mess hall on the mountain but it was impossible. In my spare time, I visited the hospitals and helped the nurses tend to the broken and the sick for there were always too many patients and not near enough medical staff to attend them.

It was there in Chattanooga sometime later that I got another sort of awful news.

One of my dearest friends on earth, Joe Pickering, had burnt to death in a building that took fire up in Elmira while he was on furlough. A double shade of mourning now rested upon my heart over the loss. He was a noble, principled young man.

Just after this news came to me, I was sent an official diagnosis from one of the doctors at the hospital who wrote that I suffered from Endo-Cardiac Disease, what they called "Soldier's Heart[1]." This said to "incapacitate me for the exposure and fatigue incident to active field service." But after all I had went through, I didn't need any doctor to tell me there was something wrong with my heart.

They gave me a horse to ride for the coming winter on account of my poor health. The distraction of the presidential election then come along in November and nary a soul around the parts where I was voted for McClellan who was running against our

Honest Abe. I thought the ratio ran ten to one against Mac amongst the soldiers who voted in the hospitals. We had by then a heap of prisoners of war in Chattanooga and about half of them even voted for Old Abe!

For a second or two I forgot my personal troubles as we were very excited tho we had no fears as to the result of the voting. It seemed to me that I could hardly endure not being able to enjoy the elective franchise on account of my age.

Abe the Patriot won his bid for re-election.

I thought for sure then the North would soon be flooded with refugees emigrating there from the South. Hundreds went through the city daily bound for the North. Their condition was ludicrous and above all awful. The folks of the North never saw such times or suffering. I hoped they never would for it was fearsome.

The larger share of the citizens coming through Chattanooga said they had prayed God to elect Lincoln that justice may be done. Some of the women were of the old revolutionary stamp and talked patriotism as fast as a sewing machine can stitch. I got so tired talking to them I had to hold up my lower maxillary before the ligaments gave out.

We learned that the regiment had swung loose with Sherman and went to some important point, we thought Savannah[2] was their destination.

Edgerton and Tenbrook went along. Tenbrook had got himself detailed onto some general's staff out at the front. He always was the best soldier amongst us four, I guessed the officers had took notice again.

But Wiggins did not go with them this time. Instead, he finagled himself a new assignment back in Chattanooga. We picked up our friendship but especially to Wiggins, the tall tale teller, I didn't let on what I had learnt in the mess hall up on Lookout.

Once the army left Atlanta, all the rail lines north and south of us were completely destroyed by rebs. Wiggins and I received neither letters from home nor news of the regiment, the city being entirely cut off by raiders tho it was so well fortified we felt safe as long as we stayed within its bounds.

We learnt in December that our boys in the 107th had got through to Savannah after three weeks, losing some fifty men along the way. Sherman laid siege to that city and took it in only three days.

General Williams was still with them which we knew to be a blessing. The 107th continued to march on through the winter with the 20th Corps. By February, when I turned 20 years old, the regiment was in South Carolina taking the city of Columbia where it was said there was a ferocious fire. They crossed over into North Carolina sometime in March with Sherman, traveling over four hundred miles[3] we heard later, under the most terrible conditions. Edgerton tells me they were constantly slowed down by rain and deep swamps, fighting all the while and taking many losses.

For all those long months of the spring spent in Chattanooga, I toiled over my reports and patients. I had not a single letter from home in all that time, nor did Wiggins. I continued to feel awful down hearted. Only Wiggins could cheer me. I was thankful for his presence and enlivening company for nothing could discourage old Wiggins from his antics and vices. I must admit I drank and smoked whenever I got the chance for the distraction of it.

By that time most of us were so wore out by war, so sick of the sight of shattered boys, and so used up we barely noticed when the end of the cursed thing finally came.

In short order during the first week of April 1865, arrived the news that General Lee had made his last stand up in Virginia and then gave up the rebel cause at Appomattox to our General Grant. We soldier boys everywhere celebrated the wonderful news but down around Chattanooga, the reb guerillas were only inflamed to worsen their desperate attacks on our rail and supply lines. The reb General Johnson, who Sherman had so dogged throughout the Carolinas, continued to fight. Reb boys I spoke to said they didn't think he'd ever cave in, nor would the secesh politicians, no matter what General Lee had seen fit to do up north.

Then within a few days of the doings at Appomattox came the worst possible news[4] from Washington!

A Copperhead fiend shot our dearly beloved Old Abe while he was watching a play and killed him. The boys in the army took it awful hard as did I and everyone. At first we could not believe such a thing occurred, and on the eve of Old Abe's reward for noble sacrifice and sticking to the Union's cause of the last four years. I felt like another of my best friends in all the world had been taken from me, or perhaps as I would at the loss of my own father.

While we grieved this most horrible of all latest event, General Sherman never let up on General Johnson, biting hard on the heels of the last surviving Southern army. Folks said that Sherman's troops tore the countryside all to pieces along his way through the Carolinas, and worse than ever out of frustration and anger over Old Abe's killing. They said Sherman meant to bring the rebs and all the citizenry to their knees so as to take the last little bit of stuffing out of them and make them cry 'Uncle Sam.' I wondered how my boys in the little 107th were doing amidst all this destruction and cruelty. I could imagine the toll taken upon the citizens of the South but not really make out what the toll would be for the destroyers. Somehow I felt it would be large.

Finally, General Johnson admitted his poor reb boys could not take another step or fire another shot. He surrendered to Sherman on April 26th. The war was mostly over but it had taken so much with it, including, unbelievably, our hero Old Abe.

Wiggins and I walked out together through the city the night the word of surrender come, where the mood was excited but we admitted to each other a certain feeling of numbness as if the victorious day had come too late. Too late to save Old Abe, too late to save so many of us, even a nagging feeling that the cost had been too high to save the country. As if the original idea of the country had been overly broken and trampled upon. I tried to put such thoughts from me and join in the celebrations, hoping to go home soon.

But those cruel and contemptible villains, the rebel raiders and guerrillas in the south did not give up, even then. We couldn't go home right away on account of them but had to stay in Chattanooga for another couple of months with flare ups of fighting going on in the countryside all the while.

I still feared the Coppers and Southerners too much to breath a word of what I knew about my involvement in Stonewall's death, even after the peace was made between the governments. I didn't want to end up murdered out of bitterness and revenge like our President.

At long last they mustered me and Wiggins out in June and sent us home together from Chattanooga by the railroad. The rest of the boys in the regiment were called up from North Carolina to Washington and mustered out there. They were soon sent along home. In Waverly, we were one and all welcomed like heroes with much fanfare. There was even a parade in our honor which was attended by all of my family and Amy came up from Pennsylvania.

When at last I saw Tenbrook, he never looked better, fit as a fiddle. He enjoyed such a hearty constitution that he must have thrived on the worst sort of hardship. But Edgerton told me his own health was broke down like mine from fever, his shoulder wound, and the fearful conditions of the long march with Sherman. Tho we were awful glad to see each other again, we felt sorry because we learnt the regiment had half of its original thousand killed, wounded, or missing. There were many more present but mustered out like myself and Edgerton who suffered from all sorts of other problems of ill health, injuries, poor spirits, and heartbreak.

At home, I went ahead and took the two Wills and Wiggins into my confidence, telling them of the strange roll I played in the fall of Stonewall Jackson. But I was still terrified lest it get out further and bring the hand of vengeance down upon me, my future wife or any children we might have. I therefore swore my friends to secrecy and they have kept good faith, even Wiggins, fearing, as I do, that I might be murdered for it. I think I may speak of it more openly at some point, once I know all the hard feeling over the war has washed away but that will most likely be never.

Edgerton says he is going to open a store to sell boots and shoes & such in the next town over to Waverly. As a noble and faithful son, he's going to get to it on the double on account of his family needing money so desperately. His mother and siblings have no where in the world to live, his father having spent up everything and run off like a scoundrel. Wiggins went back to Mary and their little child. Tenbrook is on the farm again with his family. I hope my friends will be alright once they settle in after their lengthy ordeal.

I'm thinking I might set up in the drug business after all tho I still feel drawn toward a closer study of medicine from all my experiences in the war hospitals. The great mountain of suffering and death I have witnessed, well, I feel I must try to get over it somehow. Being around the doctors, wounded, and sick has got a sort of hold on my mind. It would come good to ease some pain and help folks out. If my heart ever heals from this disease I may look into it further.

In spite of my poor health, Amy and I laid plans soon after I got back. We will wed in a year. My father has softened on the subject since I have made it home mostly alive and we two are so strongly set upon our union as man and wife. Father admitted to me that he felt proud of all that I had endured and sacrificed and that I was certainly growed enough now to marry.

Today, it seems to me a fanciful and childish dream that three years ago, I had thoughten to go for a soldier almost on a bluff but planned to be home by the spring season. It was a simple enough sounding prospect at that time. I reckoned my part was going to be a small one of minor consequence amongst all the crowds of boys who went out to fight the war. It certainly turned out different than anything I could have imagined. Especially as my fate was intertwined with the fate of that great soldier and Christian man, Stonewall Jackson.

Well, as I have said before, you might think you had heard of the horrors of war, all the games played, and the terrible cost of it, but when you get there, and see it for yourself, you would think you never heard nothing about it.

1. Soldier's Heart

The diagnosis was not an uncommon one to be given to convalescent Civil War soldiers. It was also known as "Irritable Heart." Symptoms of the condition included faintness, dizzy spells upon exertion, shortness of breath, heart palpitations and murmurs, chest pain, sweats, and stomach related difficulties.

Because it was such a conglomerate of symptoms, it was named Da Costa's Syndrome, after the surgeon who first described it as a specific condition. Doctors at the time thought that most soldiers developed it after suffering an acute bout of diarrhea.

The actual notice from Rufus's doctor read:

US General Hospital No 3 Lookout Mountain Oct 30th, 1864

This certifies that I have this day examined R S Harnden, Private, Co. A, 107th New York Vols; and find him suffering from endocardiac disease - which, in my opinion, incapacitates him for the exposure and fatigue incident to active field service.

In modern times, the syndrome is recognized as Post Traumatic Stress.

2. Savannah and the March to the Sea

The 107th NY Regiment, fighting and marching for 3 weeks en route to Savannah with Sherman, lost 6 men and 1 officer to wounds, with a total of 52 missing by end of the journey on December 10th. Upon arrival, Sherman laid siege to Savannah. The city could only hold out for 3 days. Sherman then offered it to President Lincoln as a Christmas present.

In the middle of January, Sherman began his famous Campaign of the Carolinas. This would prove to be the final campaign of the Western Theater. The ultimate goal was to push through into Virginia and link up with General Grant's forces at Richmond. Once there, Sherman would help Grant deliver a final blow to the resolve of the Southern rebels.

Meanwhile, along the way to Virginia, Sherman meant to exhaust the Confederacy ever more deeply with his scorched earth tactics, in particular he meant to punish South Carolina, which he considered to be the ringleader of the rebellion. It had been the first state to secede and the state that had opened fire on Fort Sumpter in 1861.

Once again, Sherman confounded his opposition by keeping his plans a secret and by dividing his forces and sending them off after different targets. Though he started with just over 60,000 men, he received enough reinforcements to bring his number up to close to 90,000 by April. At the same time, General Johnston's Army of the Tennessee was getting much smaller, receiving few reinforcements and only amounting to 15,000 men by April.

3. 400 Miles

By March the Union army crossed into North Carolina. On March 16th, the 107th NY fought at the Battle of Averysboro, N.C. and suffered 5 killed and 24 wounded with 18 more men missing by the close of hostilities.

March also saw the regiment engaged at Bentonville, as well as acting as part of the occupation of Goldsboro and then Raleigh, N.C. By the end of March, Sherman's men had marched over 400 miles in 50 days, with many engagements along the way. The going had been incredibly difficult, the men being constantly bogged down by rain in mud, rice fields, and swamps.

General Williams wrote a long passage in his letters that described the condition and character of the Union advance through the Carolinas:

"Our campaign has been more arduous, weather worse, and roads infamously worse than on the Georgia campaign. We have but little fighting, however, so far, the enemy always easily driven away from the strongest positions. He has evidently been confounded by the audacity of our movements. We swept through South Carolina, the fountainhead of rebellion, in a broad, semi-circular belt, sixty miles wide...

Our people, impressed with the idea that every South Carolinian was an errant Rebel, spared nothing but the old men, women, and children. All materials, all vacant houses, factories, cotton gins and presses, everything that makes the wealth of a people, everything edible and wearable, was swept away.

The soldiers quietly took the matter into their own hands. Orders to respect houses and private property not necessary for subsistence of the army were not greatly heeded. Indeed, not heeded at all. Our 'bummers,' dare-devils and reckless of the army, put the flames to everything and we marched with thousands of columns of smoke marking the line of each corps."

4. The Worst Possible News

Incredibly, as if Lincoln's life and purpose were inexorably intertwined with the war's final days, Lincoln was assassinated in Washington on April 14th, 1864, only 5 days after Lee gave up in Virginia.

The war continued in the Carolinas for 12 more days.

The Assassination of President Abraham Lincoln by actor John Wilkes Booth, at Ford's Theatre

John Wilkes Booth

Stonewall's Horse Little Sorrell

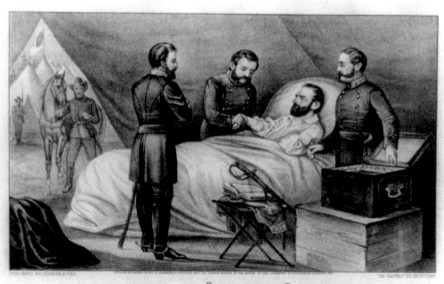

THE DEATH OF "STONEWALL JACKSON."

Death of Stonewall Jackson

General Robert E. Lee, Commander of the Army of Virginia

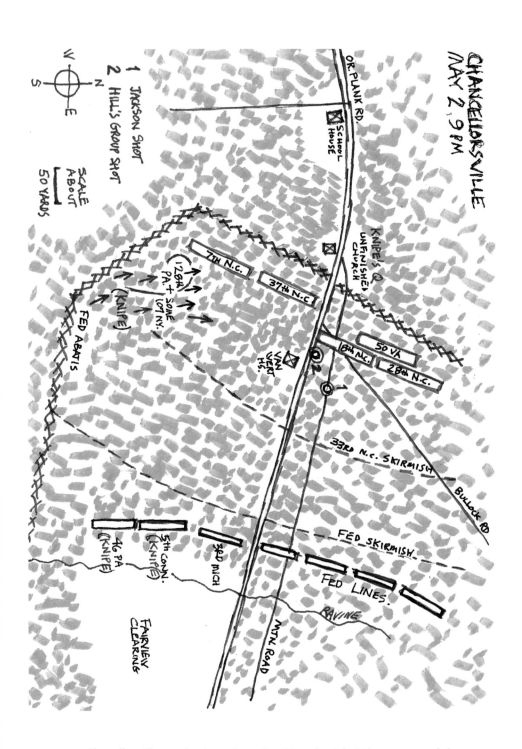

Chancellorsville map showing regimental positions the night Jackson was wounded

Conclusion

In 1865, Rufus arrived back home in Waverly, New York. He married his sweetheart, Amy Bosworth, on Christmas Day of 1866 as planned. Then he went into the drugstore business in Pennsylvania with his new brother in law, J P Bosworth. He endured two more years of ill health working as an apothecary and then, when he was feeling better, turned his attention to medicine, studying at his father's side and also at New York's Bellevue Medical College. He graduated from there in 1873 and set up his own private practice back in Waverly. He was no longer troubled by the heart disease that had been diagnosed by the army doctors. He and Amy had five children of which two died in childhood.

During his lengthy and successful career as a doctor, he wrote extensively for medical journals and also served as a surgeon for the Erie Railroad. In 1889, he advised the railroad company to fumigate all the street cars, coaches, and sleeping cars once a week in order to disinfect them. The railroad followed his advise and carried out the precaution. Henceforth the State Health Department of New York credited him with saving over fifty thousand lives a year by preventing the spread of diseases among those many travelers using the cars.

In 1899, Rufus Harnden obtained a double volume set of books called "Stonewall Jackson and the American Civil War." In it, there is a passage about the night of May, 2nd, 1863 from a chapter called 'The Fatal Volley,' that goes like this: "After a few minutes, becoming impatient for the advance of Hill's Division, Jackson turned and retraced his steps toward his own lines. "General," said an officer who was with him, "You should not expose yourself so much." (Jackson replied) "There is no danger, sir, the enemy is routed. Go back and tell General Hill to press on." Once more, when he was only 60 or 80 yards from where the 18th North Carolinians were standing in the trees, he drew rein and listened - the whole party, generals, staff-officers, and couriers, hidden in the deep shadows of the silent woods. At this moment a single rifle shot rang out with startling suddenness." Rufus took up a pencil and carefully wrote in the margins of the page:

"I fired that shot against orders and after a long conference with Jackson's chief of aides at the time, the major declared, "Your shot killed Jackson and you might better have killed 50,000 of our troops!"

Then he continued to read:

"A detachment of Federal infantry, groping their way through the thickets, had approached the Southern lines. The skirmishers on both sides were now engaged, and the lines of battle in the rear became keenly on the alert."

Here Rufus made another note:

"The Major and I agree there were no pickets or skirmishers at that point."

He read further:

"Some mounted officers galloped hastily back to their commands. The sound startled the Confederate soldiers, and an officer of the 18th NC, seeing a group of strange horsemen riding toward him through the darkness - for Jackson, hearing the firing, had turned back to his own lines - gave the order to fire. The volley was fearfully effective. Men and horses fell dead and dying on the narrow track. Jackson himself received three bullets, one in the right hand, and two in the left arm."

Then Rufus drew a line to the words "three bullets" and wrote:

"From a volley from our line, so the Major and I agree."

In the flyleaf of volume 1, he also wrote:

"As Lt Gen Jacksons Chief of aids claims. My one lonely shot killed the General. I wish to say tho I was a corporal in 107th US

Vol Inf - had I known it was General Jackson, I would not have fired that bullet. We had reason ample for greatly admiring the good Christian Gen'l: as kindly a man as ever lived (the many lickings he gave us, attest his greatness etc.)"

Further along in the book, in the chapter on Gettysburg, there was a passage that quoted General Lee as saying:
"If I had had Jackson at Gettysburg I should have won the battle, and a complete victory there would have resulted in the establishment of Southern Independence."

Rufus drew another line to this quotation and then wrote along the margin:

"Jackson's chief aid de camp tells me there is no doubt that my one shot killed Jackson. Dr. RS Harnden. Corps A 107th NY Vols. We Yanks greatly admired Jackson. I would not have shot him had I known it was him. I had just escaped from there."

It is most likely that Rufus had the opportunity to talk to Jackson's aide, the man he referred to as the Major, at one of the many reunions held for the soldiers after the war. Remarkably, some of these were attended by veterans from both sides. There were several held for survivors of Chancellorsville during the 1880's.

Although he made notes in the books, Rufus never went public with what he knew of the famous night in the woods.

In 1890, the survivors of the 107th NY had their own reunion in Elmira. Rufus attended and was presented with a picture of the regimental banner, the very one that was "cut to strings" above his head at Antietam. He made some notes upon it and kept it for the rest of his life.

Rufus retired from private practice in 1915 after a distinguished career as a doctor. He died at the age of eighty-three, quite deaf by that time, most likely from damage to his hearing sustained during the battles, as was the case with so many Civil War veterans.

❦

Rufus and Amy's Harnden's eldest daughter Ruth grew up to marry Bradley Phillips, an attorney from Buffalo NY. They had two children only one of whom survived childhood. His name was Philip Phillips, born 1900. Philip became an archeologist and fathered three children, Patricia, Sayre, and Bradley.

Dr. Phillips inherited the large collection of his grandfather's Civil War letters. He and a friend, Horace Middleton, worked diligently to put Rufus's letters in order and transcribe them as many of them were faded and barely legible. Dr. Phillips eventually gave the letters and their transcription to his son in law, Stanley Sheldon, the husband of his daughter Sayre. Stanley was a history teacher and an avid student of the Civil War. He spent time researching the details of where Rufus was during the two major battles he fought in. Of course, Stanley was particularly fascinated by Rufus's certainty that he fired the famous lone gunshot at Chancellorsville which may have mortally wounded Stonewall Jackson.

I found the collection of letters among my father's papers after he died and began the long process of trying to put the material into a cohesive narrative so that Rufus could at last tell his story. I had a great deal of help and encouragement from my mother, Sayre Phillips Sheldon.

Battle Flag of the 107th N. Y. Vols.

On the 17th day of September, 1862, just twenty-eight years ago, this flag was carried by the 107th New York Volunteers into the battle of Antietam. The regiment was advancing in the direction of the Dunker Church, under a heavy fire from the enemy. A shell from a battery in their front exploded directly over the flag, tearing it to pieces as shown in the cut. It is now in keeping of the State at Albany.

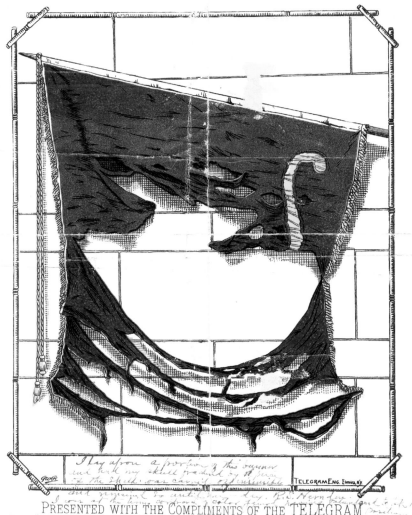

PRESENTED WITH THE COMPLIMENTS OF THE TELEGRAM

To the Survivors of the 107th Regiment, New York Volunteers, on the Occasion of their Reunion, Held in the city of Elmira, Wednesday, September 17th, 1890.

Battle Flag of the 107th NY Volunteers

Dr. Rufus Harnden in Middle Age

Rufus in Old Age

Rufus with Wife, Daughter, and Grandson, Philip Phillips, 1903

LEE IS LEFT ALONE   579

burg I should have won the battle, and a complete victory
there would have resulted in the establishment of Southern
independence.'

It was not to be. Chancellorsville, where 130,000 men
were defeated by 60,000, is up to a certain point as much
the tactical masterpiece of the nineteenth century as was
Leuthen of the eighteenth. But, splendid triumph as it
was, the battle bore no abiding fruits, and the reason seems
now clear. The voice that would have urged pursuit was

Rufus's notes in a book about Stonewall Jackson

Sept 19 1862

Antietam Battle field sept 19

Dear Father I am now at a hospital where
there is over a thousand wounded men & a great
many dying all the time I have past to stay
witnessed about 12 or 15 Amputations of limbs
mostly legs there is 8 or 9 other hospitals that
I know of and some of them have more
wounded in than this, since the battle I have
been assisting the surgeons in 2 or 3 diferent
hospitals, I am wounded myself though it
was slight it was a verry narrow escape the
shell that tore our colors to pieces came
near tearing me also a few days before that
I was detailed for color guard and was lying
flat on the ground close to the
colors, when the shell exploded, a piece struck
me about 2 inches square, it grazed my
cheek & across my eyelid about like a
deepin scratch & cut the eye brow in to
the bone & up under the bone so as to make
my head feel dizzy for 3 or 4 days, the same
shell killed 1 or 2 men and wounded some
others verry bad

Md. 46th   Oct 2.d   62

Dear Parents, I do not feel able
to write any more but as their
has been some news I will the
President was here this morning
I saw him & his whole staff
they were fine looking fellows
but I would like to see them
do the fighting. there are rumors
about here that Gen. Lee &
his staff are in washington
with a flag of truce ~~and~~ & another was that they had sued
for peace & that they would
pay the dept as fast as they
could(you may think by this
letter and the one of yesterday
that I am finding fault ~~with~~
at an awfull rate but that
is not so, What I have wrote

I wish the big politicians
had to fight it out, and
that is what the soldiers all
think seeesh as well as ours
I have talked with a great many
of the prisoners & wounded rebs.
as they all wish the leaders had
to fight it out, I have had one
streak of good luck they found
an over coat some of the company
did and it had an R & an H on
it they said it was mine &
sent it over to me, well. I think
I shall hang on to it as cold
wether is coming on pretty fast I
have got my name sewed in
it in large letters so they will
know it is mine now, I do not
know whether the regt will go into
winter quarters here, or be sent to
washington we are in hopes we
will go to washington

T. K. Beecher Chaplin of the 141st regt from Elmira, but it rained all day our chaplain is sick in washington. We have not had a sermon in a long time a Mr. Barnes a private in the regt took prayers the for a while but he was taken sick & died. I will try & give you a discription of our log house we had to carry the logs a good ways.

the tent is 7 feet by 6 & the logs are 2 feet high or all around the line poles that we could carry. the pen frast is 2 feet high & then we put up our tents on top of the logs. the stove in the corner, we havent got but we will build a fire place there in the other corner is a cupboard & on that side We sleep right on the ground to. Wizens on the back side Edgerton next & I in front. this is very comfortable quarters. that discription of tent is a terrible thing. We have 6 roll calls a day drill one hour in the morning 1½ in the forenoon the same in the afternoon dress Parade at dark. Roll call at 8 oclock. taps at ½ past

Office Quel Dir of Post.
Chattanooga. Tennessee, June 3rd 64

Dear Parents.

And others at Home Excuse
me for writing thus soon again. As I have
Something I think will Interest you in Some
Way. At least it does me very much Indeed
The 18·7th has seen one of the Sharpest Engagemts
it ever has & been cut up very bad {143}
being the number "Killed & Wounded". I will send
you a paper with list which is not all. There
are a good many I have seen that are not down.
I went to night to find Same & all that I found
were minus a leg or arm & Some both I found
nine or ten, The Slight Wounded we have sent
to Nashville to Hospitals there.
Yesterday afternoon I found "Captain Losie" Lying
in one of the Wards which I pass & repass
going to my meals. He knew me in a moment
and we had a very cordial greeting. he had his
Right Leg taken off above the knee about five inches
he is doing very well at present. Last night I
went to the City & got Some Dried fruit of different

Siege of Atlanta

Aug 24th 1864

Friend Rufus

Once more
I sit down "in the
trenches" to write a
few lines to an old
friend and tent mate
on whome the fortunes
of war have less
severe than on my
self. Still I cannot
complain as I have
never had a scratch
from a Rebel Bullet
or Shell. My health
is very good at present
but for about a week
past I have not been
very well having been
troubled with that
malady so well known
to all of Uncle Sam's

Oct 5 .64

L. Mtn,
Georgia
Oct 5/64

Dear Mother. I thought
I would write you a line
this eve & but a line for
I feel sad! a shade of
mourning rests upon myheart;
over the loss of my old Correspondent
& now my Dearest friends on earth
# Jno Pickering; We have had a
pleasant Correspondence & goodtime
We expected to have more but he
is gone Me was my bestfriend
and a noble principled young
man was he. I can hardly believe
it and I want you to write & tell
Me if it is so and the particulars
concerning the disaster oh! how I
sympathize with his Parents it must
be awful to them. twill distract his good mother

No 2

I have made up my
mind to go through
it & not flinch I have
stood the march so far better
than I expected my feet
are blistered verry bad
. I gave to day a dolar between
an old pair of shoes not as
good as mine but larger
we are at a place called
Kellys ford we are not alowed
to have a fire or or loud
talk it is the report that
the enemy are on the other
side in large force old
Joe Hooker is with us
he passed by us this after
& such yelling you never (mum
heard it was a regular
Bayonett charge yell from
whole division.

Campbell Hospital
Washington D.C.
Dec. 11th
1863

To whom it may concern:

This is to certify that
Corp. R. S. Harnden 107th N.Y.
was on duty as clerk in the Dispensary of this Hospital & thus
proved himself a man of strict
integrity, & sobriety, We the undersigned take pleasure in recommending him as an industrious, faithful
& competent man in the discharge
of the duties assigned him while
here.

Very Respectfully
Yours &c,

J. H. Baxter
Surg. U.S.V. in chg Hospl
N M Gaylord
Chaplain U Sa
Geo. J. Wood Hospl Steward U.S.A.

you need not direct Mr Wiggins papers

I suppose you think I am getting
home sick, but taint so

~~trouble~~
and are ~~and~~ genealy fat
they will burn easy

Well I guess I'll stop or, I'll
run into wiggins style,

but, I have not written
anything in this letter but
what is true, I have not in
any other, you may think
by what I say about wiggins
that we have had a fuss or some
trouble but we have not we
have been on good terms &
are now. I can not blame him
much if he has gone, but I ~~aint~~ am
~~not going to desert~~
going, it is getting late & I must
close, I think we will get our pay soon
give my respects to all. See I
wrote fred the other day, don't say
any thing about wiggins untill
you see him, yours &c. R. Harnden

& let me know how he gets along

W. O. L—

he will have a good deal
to say about the Battle of
Antietam. acording to his own
story he was in the fight a short
time & fainted away & was carried
off by an old soldier. & remained
insensible 18 hours. & yet he
can tell 5 times as much about
it as any of the rest of us
he will tell things that any
sensible man would know
was imposible. he says eleven bomb
shells struck within 10 feet
of his head. I saw all of the
shells. or rather saw where
they struck & I did not see
any strike so close. as he tells
about. nor did any of the
company. there was one struck
pretty close to the colors I reckon

Tell about. Hewitt to write to me

Bibliography

Websites

Antietam on the Web, Official Officers' reports (antietam.aotw.org)

Chancellorsville on the Web, Official Officers' Reports (http://www.civilwarhome.com/chancell.htm)

Civil War Trust (civilwar.org/chancellorsville)

Harper's Weekly (via sonofthesouth.net)

HistoryNet (historynet.com)

Home of the American Civil War (civilwarhome.com)

The Library of Congress (loc.gov)

The National Park Service (nps.gov)

National Archives (archives.gov)

New York State Military Museum (dana.ny.gov/historic/civil/infantry/107thnlfMain.htm)

Ohio State University Department of History (history.osu.edu)

USA Civil War (www.usa-civil-war.com/Civil_War/definitions.shtml)

US Army Center of Military History (history.army.mil)

Letters

Pat Bozeman, Emily Scott Evans Endowed Professor and Head of Special Collections at University of Houston Libraries. The letters of Will Edgerton, another member of the 107th NY Regiment.

Books

Banta, Theodore. Sayre Family The De Vinne Press. New York. 1901

Bigalow, John. The Campaign of Chancellorsville: A Strategic and Tactical Study Univ. of Yale Press. 1910

Coggins, Jack. Arms and Equipment of the Civil War Broadfoot Publishing Co. NC. 1962

Colby, Lt. Col. Newton T. The Civil War Papers of Lt. Colonel Newton T. Colby, New York Infantry North Carolina and London. McFarland and Company, Inc. 2003

Dabney, Prof R. L. The Life and Campaigns of Lieut.-General Thomas J. Jackson National Publishing Co. 1866

Dodge, Theodore A. <u>The Campaign of Chancellorsville</u> 1881

Gallager, Gary W. <u>Chancellorsville, The Battle and Its Aftermath</u>
Chapel Hill and London. The University of North Carolina Press.1996

Haines, Joe D. <u>America's Civil War: Stonewall Jackson's Last Days</u>
American Civil War Magazine

Hamlin, Augustas Choate. <u>The Battle of Chancellorsville</u>
Published by the Author. Bangor, ME. 1896

Heidler, David S. and Jeanne T. eds. <u>Encyclopedia of the American</u>
<u>Civil War</u> New York and London. W. W. Norton and Company. 2000

Henderson, Lieut.-Col G. F. R. <u>Stonewall Jackson and the American</u>
<u>Civil War</u> 2 Volumes. London: Longman's, Green, and Co. 1899

Kagan, Neil. ed <u>Eyewitness to the Civil War: The Complete History</u>
<u>from Secession to Reconstruction</u> National Geographic Society. 2006.

Krick, Robert K. <u>The Smoothbore Volley That Doomed the Confederacy</u>
Baton Rouge. Louisiana State University Press. 2002.

McPherson, James M.
<u>This Mighty Scourge</u> New York. Oxford University Press. 2007
<u>Crossroads of Freedom: Antietam</u> New York. Oxford University Press. 2002
<u>Battle Cry of Freedom</u> New York. Oxford University Press. 1988

Moat, Louis, ed. <u>Frank Leslie's Illustrated History of the Civil War</u>
The Fairfax Press. 1977

Pratt, Fletcher. <u>Civil War in Pictures</u> Garden Books, NY. 1955

Priest, John Michael. <u>Antietam: The Soldiers' Battlefield</u>
White Mane Publishing, PA. 1994

Sears, Stephen W. <u>Chancellorsville</u> New York.
Houghton Miffler Company. 1996

Shaw, Anthony, ed. <u>The Civil War Catalogue</u> Courage Books.
Philadelphia & London. 2003

Stanchak, John, ed. <u>Leslie's Illustrated Civil War</u> Univ Press Of Mississippi.
Jackson & London.1992

Tuttle, Russell M. <u>The Civil War Journal of Lt. M. Tuttle, New York</u>
<u>Volunteer Infantry</u> North Carolina and London.
McFarland and Company, Inc. 2006

Williams, General Alpheus. <u>From The Cannon's Mouth</u>
Lincoln and London. Bison Books. University of Nebraska Press.1959

Phoebe Sheldon grew up and was educated in Cambridge and Boston.
She has art degrees from Boston University and the Oakland College
of Arts and Crafts. She is an artist who works mainly in ceramics and
has written for Ceramics Monthly. She has two daughters and lives
today in Hatfield, Massachusetts. A lifelong interest in history and
writing led her to decide that her great-great grandfather's letters
should be a book.